ALCAN AND CANOL

A Pictorial History of Two Great World War II Construction Projects

The Alaska Highway

The U. S. Army took over a strip,
  A strip of Canadian soil,
They did it without a single hitch,
  Without creating a boil,
Their engineers went on ahead,
  Surveyed and staked a trail,
The job was done in record time,
  No such thing as fail.

Soldiers followed with dozers and cats,
  Clearing the right-of-way,
Like coaches guiding a football squad,
  Officers led the play.
Over the hills and valleys deep,
  Over some raging stream,
Working together like all were one,
  Sure was a wonderful scene.

Colored boys from the south so hot,
  Working here in the cold,
Dressed in woolens and parkas warm,
  Pitched in and took a hold,
Singing the songs of Dixie land,
  'Way up here in the north,
Far from the cotton fields at home
  Soldiers that held the fort.

Mile after mile they battled on,
  Determined to see the end,
Never stopping for snow or rain,
  Backs to the task they bend,
From Dawson Creek to Fairbanks,
  Ever kicking a goal,
Heeding not the kee bird's cry,
  Screeching about the cold.

True, some graves that mark the trail,
  Someone who passed away,
Like every big job that's ever done
  Some death is the price we pay.
"Keep 'em rolling", the slogan now,
  Seeing the road is done,
Another niche in the hall of fame,
  Once more our army has won.

UNKNOWN AUTHOR, CIRCA 1940s.

ALCAN AND CANOL

A Pictorial History of Two Great World War II Construction Projects
by Stan Cohen

Pictorial Histories Publishing Company, Inc.
Missoula, Montana

LIBRARY OF CONGRESS
CATALOG CARD NO. 92-80910

ISBN 0-929521-50-1

First Printing: May 1992

Typography: Arrow Graphics
Cover Art: Steve Hillyer
Cover Design: Mike Egeler

A NOTE ABOUT THE COVER TITLE:

*ALCAN stands for Alaska-Canada Highway. Congressional legislation on July 19, 1943, formally
named the highway—the Alaska Highway—a name that has been used ever since.
CANOL stands for Canadian Oil, a wartime project to construct an oil pipeline from Norman
Wells, Northwest Territories to Whitehorse, Yukon.*

*The author accepts full responsibility for the accuracy of all facts and for all opinions expressed in
this book and acknowledges that neither Alaska Highway Rendezvous '92 Society nor any of its
associated organizations bear any responsibility for those facts or opinions.*

PICTORIAL HISTORIES PUBLISHING CO., INC.
713 South Third Street West, Missoula, MT 59801

INTRODUCTION

In 1979 I published my first book on the Alaska Highway— *The Trail of '42*. This book has gone through 15 printings and has become the largest selling book on the history of the highway construction period.

Because of this book and other books I have written on Alaska and Yukon history, I have driven up and down the highway close to 20 times, I have interviewed scores of people on the highway and have corresponded with hundreds of veterans who participated in these two great construction projects—The Alcan (Alaska) Highway and Canadian Oil (CANOL) Pipeline. Although cameras were supposedly suppressed by the authorities for both military and civilian personnel, literally hundreds upon hundreds of photos have surfaced in the last few years from individuals throughout the United States and Canada. There are also thousands of official government photographs deposited in various archives in both countries.

This 50th anniversary book is meant to be the definitive photo history of the construction projects. I have not attempted to include lengthy narratives on the different aspects as various new books mentioned below do a much better job than I could do. I have however included a few first person accounts to give the reader a more personal account of the historic events.

I have tried to include images of every possible facet of life during the construction process and views of the highway as it appears today. Many of these photos also appear in my book *The Trail of '42* but many, many photos are printed here for the first time.

My purpose in this new volume is to give the reader a visual account of the two greatest construction projects that both Americans and Canadians participated in during World War Two.

I am deeply indebted to John Schmidt of Standard, Alberta, who allowed me to use some of the text from his excellent book *This Was No ΦYXNH Picnic 2.4 Years of Wild and Woolly Mayhem in Dawson Creek*. This is without a doubt the best human interest account of the 1942-45 period on the market today. And don't let the title fool you—the book covers most of the miles of the highway in Canada, not just in Dawson Creek. The best actual historical record of the highway has to be Ken Coates' new book, *North to Alaska!*

Fifty Years on the World's Most Remarkable Highway. Several other good books on both construction projects are listed in the bibliography.

Many people contributed either photos or information or both and this book could not have been completed without them. Ken Spotswood of the Yukon Anniversaries Commission in Whitehorse provided several of the opening ceremonies photos and much information. I am deeply grateful to him for his encouragement over the last several years. My good friend and sales representative in Fort Nelson, Earl Brown, has also provided many years of well-timed encouragement.

Much help was also received from the staffs of the Yukon Archives; Glenbow Archives; Provincial Archives of Alberta and British Columbia; Alaska State Library; Alaska & Polar Regions Dept., Elmer E. Rasmuson Library, University of Alaska Fairbanks; Anchorage Museum of History and Art; National Archives of Canada; the Watson Lake Highway Interpretive Center; Delta Chamber of Commerce; Festival Fairbanks; the National Archives of the United States and the Library of Congress.

And to the following individuals for their help and support, my heartfelt thanks: Dr. Donald Mueller, West Union, Iowa, and his father, Ernest Mueller, Boone, Iowa; Garth Hall, Dawson Creek, B.C.; Jack Gunness, Muncho Lake, B.C.; Dorothy Jones, Forest Grove, Ore.; Carl Lindley, Danville, Ill.; Milton Brunson, Butte, Mont.; Michael Bevan, Mississauga, Ontario; Russ Dow, Palmer, Alaska; Gordon Priest, Edmonton, Alberta; Mrs. Jeanellen O. Killian, Novato, Calif., daughter of General O'Connor; Bill Hebert, Kalispell, Mont.; Anthony Podgurski. Ridgefield, N.J.; Sid Navratil, Pittsburgh, Pa.; Marl Brown, Fort Nelson, B.C.; Lyman Woodman, Anchorage, Alaska; Wayne Tocoriss, Whitehorse, Yukon; Helene Dobrowolsky, Whitehorse, Yukon; Donna Kyllo, North Peace Historical Society, Fort St. John, B.C.; Candy Waugaman, Fairbanks, Alaska; Rudy Marek, Banks, Ore.; Barbara Kalen, Skagway, Alaska; Ted Miduski, Ozona, Fla.; Michelle Roberts, Fairbanks, Alaska and Harold Maltbie as well as the hundreds of veterans I have corresponded with through the years. Thank you also to Ben Clark and Bob Jones for editing this manuscript.

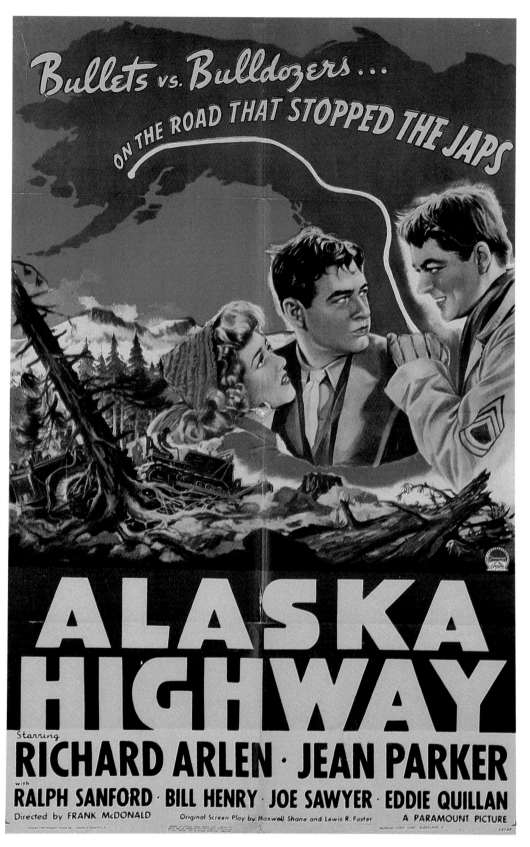

This 1943 movie was typical of wartime movies produced by
Hollywood studios. CANDY WAUGAMAN

CONTENTS

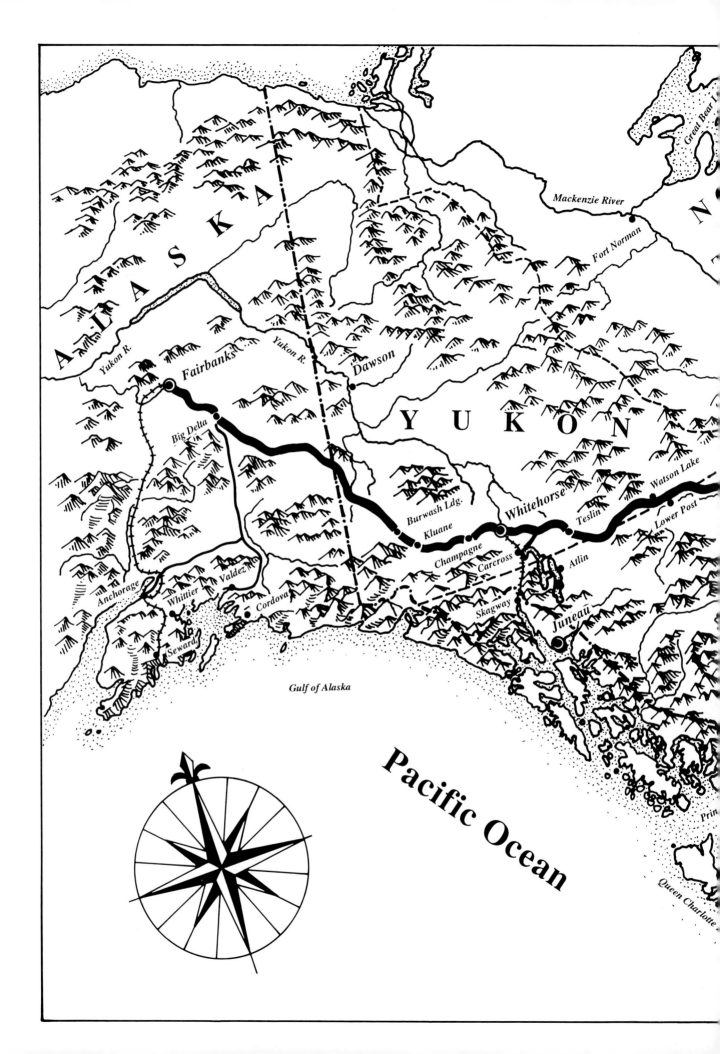

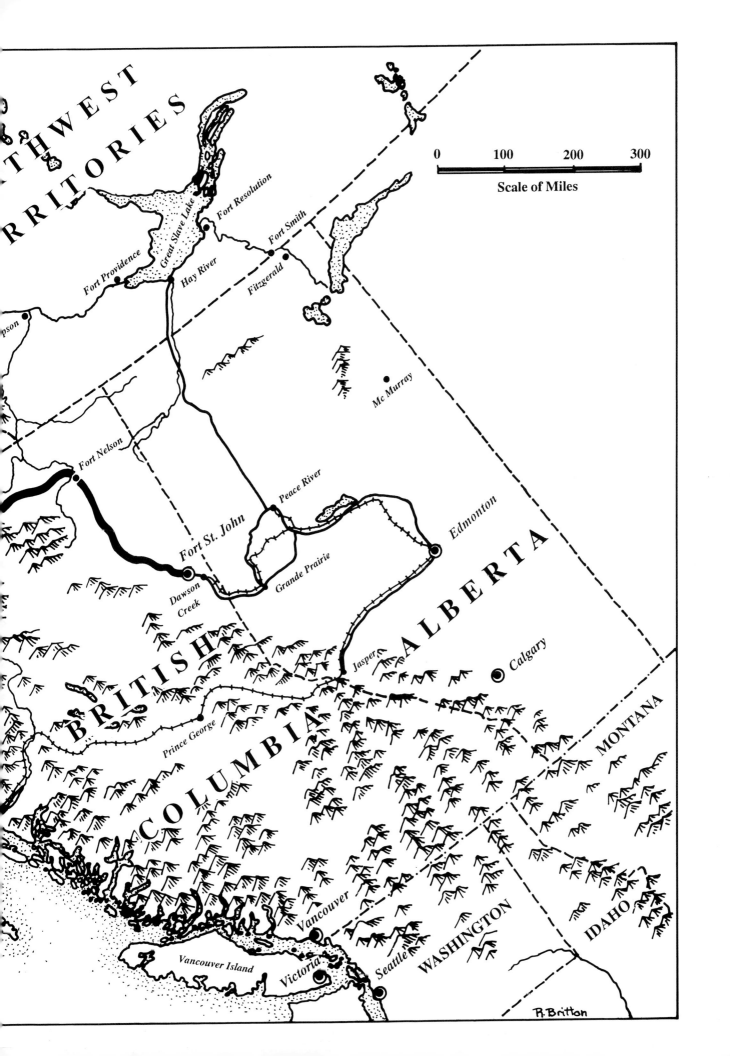

NORTHWEST TERRITORIES

Fort Providence
Great Slave Lake
Fort Resolution
Hay River
Fort Smith
Fitzgerald

pson

Mc Murray

Fort Nelson

Peace River

Fort St. John

Edmonton

Dawson Creek

Grande Prairie

ALBERTA

BRITISH

Jasper

Calgary

Prince George

COLUMBIA

MONTANA

Vancouver

Vancouver Island

Victoria

Seattle

WASHINGTON

IDAHO

R. Britton

0   100   200   300

Scale of Miles

"Roll 'er through to Fairbanks!"

Greyhound serves America-at-War along the Alcan Military Highway

THE OUTLINE MAP below shows the Alcan Highway (heavy red line, including both highways and rail links) in relation to the 65,000-mile Greyhound System and its principal bus line connections.

No, you can't ride a Greyhound Super-Coach to Alaska over the Alcan Highway . . . not today! But, just the same, these familiar blue-and-white buses are rolling on that highway—doing an important job for Uncle Sam, along the most amazing military road of all history.

Buses have followed the bulldozers on the Alcan! Operating under direction of the Northwest Service Command, they are carrying the military and civilian personnel that is building, strengthening, protecting the great road.

The Alcan Military Highway is an everlasting tribute to the courage and skill of the Army Engineers Corps—that grand body of men who shoved it through ice and

storm and homeless muskeg in impossibly fast time.

What's more, it's America's pledge to the world that we'll run the greedy little Japs clear back to Tokyo and beyond! It's a pledge, too, of cooperation and friendship between Canada and the United States—a mighty link in the chain of highways that will one day span all the Americas.

After Victory comes, who can doubt that roads and buses will work together to develop the wonderland of Western Canada and Alaska, just as they have worked to give America the most convenient and flexible peacetime transportation—*and as they are now working to carry the Nation's manpower in time of war.*

GREYHOUND

1

PRE-WAR HISTORY

Alaska Highway—Triumph of American Achievement

Reprinted from
ALASKA AND THE CANADIAN NORTHWEST
by Harold Griffin

A few men had dreamed of building a highway to Alaska for years. One of them was Donald MacDonald, an engineer who believed a road from the United States to Alaska to be a practical undertaking and presently, as Japan began to unfold its plans for world conquest across the Pacific, a necessity.

In Washington his persistent efforts to obtain consideration for this project gained for him little more than the reputation of being a fanatic. Senators and congressmen listened to this forceful gray-haired man who talked so earnestly of what construction of a highway would mean to Alaska and the United States, but few of them supported his proposals. In Alaska people were less disposed to question the judgment of the man who, as location engineer for the Alaska Road Commission, had built the Steese Highway from Fairbanks to Circle. They knew of the long trips he had made into the wilds, traversing on foot routes over which a highway might be built, and when he asserted that he had found a feasible route through British Columbia and the Yukon they did not dismiss his ideas as those of an impractical dreamer. But such a highway would cost millions of dollars. While the Alaska legislature made small appropriations to further MacDonald's work, it could not undertake to construct the highway itself. It was an international project beyond the resources and territorial limits of Alaska, with its population of only sixty-two thousand, whites, Indians and Eskimos; and until the United States and Canadian governments could be convinced that the highway was necessary, it would not be built.

Even in Alaska there was opposition to the highway. The cry was raised that if the highway were built Alaska would be thrown open to all the itinerant Okies and Arkies who would migrate there in search of new homes. It was contended that the best way to develop Alaska was to let it develop itself. These were the arguments of those concerned in keeping Alaska closed, the steamship companies which controlled transportation and the commercial interests which found a profitable market in Alaska and did not wish to see the territory develop its own industries. They were calculated to appeal to the strong individualism of the older Alaskans, but they lost much of their force when Alaskans compared their own relative stagnation with the rapid progress being made in Soviet Siberia. Obviously, to let Alaska develop itself while denying it highway connections with the continental United States was synonymous with allowing Alaska to remain undeveloped.

Rebuffed time and again, MacDonald doggedly continued the work which had become the absorbing interest of his life. Delving into history, he discovered that in 1892 Tsar Alexander III of Russia had proposed an international railroad across Siberia and Alaska, a proposal revived in a report made to Tsar Nicholas II in 1900 and later discussed with the Tsarist government by E.J. Harriman, the American railroad promoter who wanted to build the railroad through Canada and Alaska. Long before Vice-President Henry A. Wallace suggested an international highway between the Americans and Asia and Europe, MacDonald envisaged it as a possibility and wrote to the Soviet government to find out what new Siberian highways might be linked at the Bering Strait with an Alaskan highway, as then unbuilt, to Nome.

Slowly the proposal for a highway to Alaska won support in the United States and Canada. In 1933, when a commission of engineers, appointed three years previously by President Herbert Hoover, reported favorably on construction of the highway, hopes were stirred that it might be built. Congress authorized the president to negotiate with the Canadian government but nothing came of the negotiations. Then, in 1937,

Japan invaded China and advocates of the highway were provided with a potent argument. As the Japanese armies marched deeper into China, Alaska became conscious of the insecurity of their empty spaces behind mountain ramparts that were no barrier to planes. Other voices joined MacDonald's in urging construction of the highway. Businessmen in Pacific coast cities formed associations to promote it and labor organizations began pressing for it as a defense against Japanese aggression and a project which would absorb thousands of unemployed.

In 1938 President Franklin D. Roosevelt appointed a second International Highway Commission with Congressman Warren G. Magnuson as chairman and Governor Ernest Gruening of Alaska, former Governor Thomas Riggs and James Carey as members. The fifth member of the commission was Donald MacDonald. Hon. Charles Stewart, former premier of Alberta, was chairman of a similar commission appointed by the Canadian government, the other members of which were J.M. Wardle of the Department of Mines and Resources, Brigadier General T.L. Tremblay, Arthur Dixon and J.H. Spencer. Both commissions conducted extensive surveys of the several routes proposed for the highway and both favored construction, the American commission over the "A" route from Hazelton, B.C., to Whitehorse, Dawson City and Fairbanks. Neither commission over the more easterly "B" route from Prince George, B.C., to Dawson City and Fairbanks. Neither commission recommended the "C" route over which the highway has now been built.

But across the Pacific, Japan, even then preparing for war against the United States, had been following these developments closely. Alaska, defenseless and unlinked with the great industrial centers of the United States, represented no insuperable obstacle to its plans. Alaska, supplied over relatively secure land routes, threatened its entire scheme with disaster. For decades this fear of encirclement through Alaska had haunted the Japanese general staff. At the Portsmouth Conference in 1905 at the end of the Russo-Japanese War this led it to exact an oral agreement that Russia would not attempt to construct its section of the Canadian-Alaskan-Russian railroad proposed by E.H. Harriman. And now that it seemed a highway might be built, the Japanese government quietly exerted its influence to halt it. Hirochiro Nemichi, the Japanese consul at Vancouver, B.C., until his recall in 1939, was instructed to fly to Whitehorse and make a direct report on the proposed highway to his government. At the same time the Japanese government entered a strong protest to the Chamberlain government at London stating that it would consider construction of a highway to Alaska as being inimical to Japanese interests. Whatever representations were made to Washington and Ottawa, the highway was not built—not then. It was built in 1942, a splendid compensation for the wasted years, when the fate of Alaska and perhaps of the Pacific coast depended upon its being completed in time.

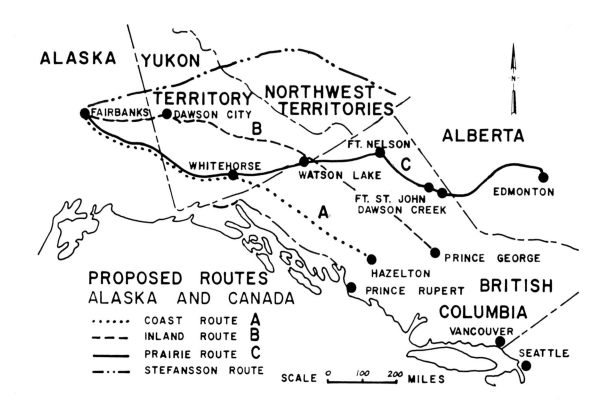

PROPOSED ROUTES
ALASKA AND CANADA

······ COAST ROUTE A
‐ ‐ ‐ INLAND ROUTE B
——— PRAIRIE ROUTE C
—··— STEFANSSON ROUTE

SCALE 0 100 200 MILES

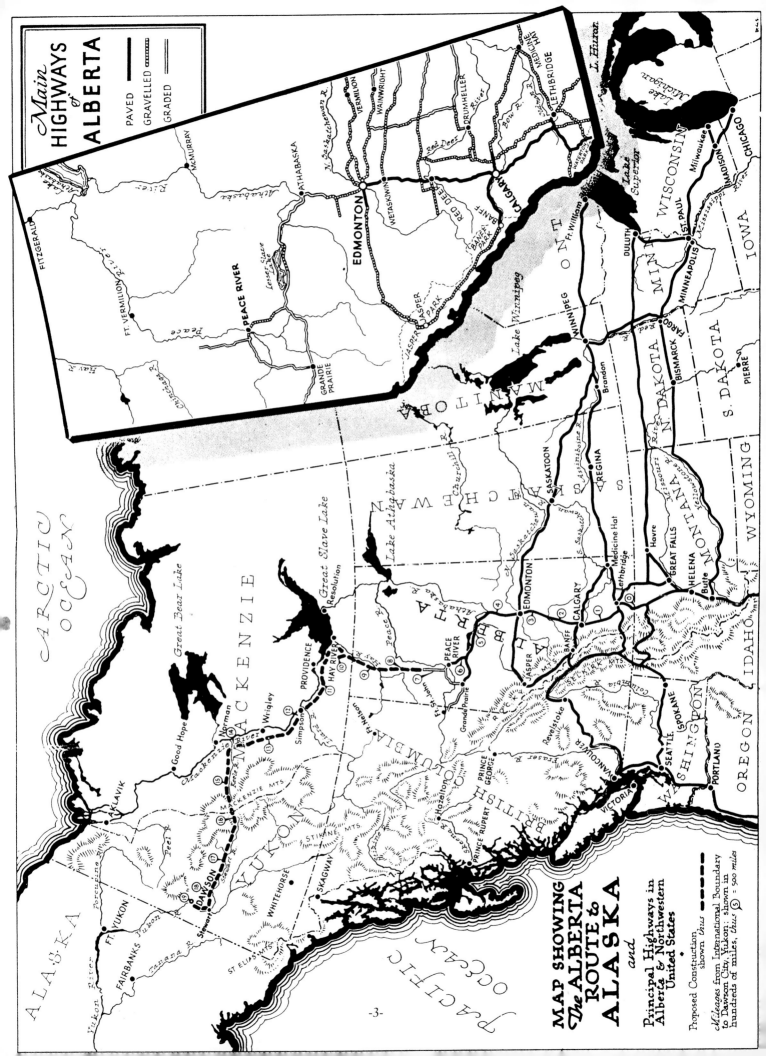

Main HIGHWAYS of ALBERTA

PAVED ▬▬▬
GRAVELLED ┄┄┄┄
GRADED ┄┄┄┄

MAP SHOWING The ALBERTA ROUTE to ALASKA and Principal Highways in Alberta & Northwestern United States

Proposed Construction shown thus ▬ ▬ ▬

Mileages from International Boundary to Dawson City, Yukon; shown in hundreds of miles, thus ⑤ = 500 miles

-3-

REPORT

OF

THE COMMISSION TO STUDY THE
PROPOSED HIGHWAY TO ALASKA

1933

I. CONCLUSIONS AND RECOMMENDATIONS

The Special Commissioners appointed by the President of the United States for a study regarding the construction of a highway to connect the northwestern part of the United States with British Columbia, Yukon Territory, and Alaska have reached the following conclusions:

1. The highway is a feasible project and can be built at a reasonable cost, which should not exceed $2,000,000 for the Alaska section and $12,000,000 for the Canadian section. Considering the highway to begin at Seattle, Washington, and end at Fairbanks, Alaska, the approximate mileage of completed road and new construction needed for completion is as follows:

Route	Completed road	New construction needed	Total
	Miles	*Miles*	*Miles*
Seattle to Hazelton, British Columbia	882	0	882
Vancouver to Hazelton, British Columbia	830	0	830
Yukon to Yukon Boundary	50	520	570
Alaska Boundary to Alaska Boundary	50	480	530
Alaska Boundary to Fairbanks	91	183	274
Seattle to Fairbanks	1,073	1,183	2,256
Vancouver to Fairbanks	1,021	1,183	2,204

2. If the project is adopted, the stage-construction process is favored. That is to say, the initial standard should be no higher than is required for the estimated traffic, and improvements to higher standards would be made as demanded by traffic and as funds may become available.

3. Financing is primarily the responsibility of each of the nations concerned for the section of the road within its own jurisdiction, and any departure from this principle, should be covered by international agreement. The Alaska section of the road should be financed in about the same ratio between federal and local funds as obtains under the Federal Highway Act in the sparsely settled States, resulting probably in about 90 percent of the cost of construction being paid by the Federal Government.

4. There are two general routes for the northern end of the highway, either of which would serve to open new Alaskan territory of importance and contribute to the general development. The Dawson-Fairbanks route possesses the advantage of more comprehensive service to Yukon Territory and the Fortymile and Chicken Creek mining areas in Alaska. The Whitehorse-Kluane Lake-Gulkana-Fairbanks route involves less new road construction in Alaska, saves several hundred miles of new construction, and also serves important mining territory in Alaska. Both routes are acceptable from the American viewpoint.

5. The benefits to be gained from the project from the American point of view are:

(a) Development of Alaska through making the territory accessible by highway, resulting in an increase of population and consequent increase in revenue from taxes, tending to decrease the present necessity for Federal appropriations for the support of the territory.

(b) The road would be a great contribution to the welfare of American citizens now living in Alaska under adverse conditions, by providing a physical connection with the vast continental road system.

(c) Opening of new country that is now practically inaccessible, giving opportunity for settlement, investment of capital and employment.

(d) The new road would make accessible to the continental highway system the existing road net in central Alaska comprising about 900 miles, providing a new and valuable area for exploration, for recreation, or for business purposes.

(e) The highway would foster air commerce with Alaska by furnishing a guiding landmark and providing service to aviators along the most practicable flying route to the interior of the territory and to Asia.

(f) Promotion of friendly relations between citizens of United States and Canada.

No attempt is made to evaluate the benefits Canada would derive from this project, but it may be mentioned that in addition to such direct development of new Canadian territory as might be brought about by the road, Canada would gain the business and commerce incident to providing service and supplies to motorists using the road for access to Alaska.

6. Since the annual cost of operating Federal agencies in Alaska is about $7,000,000 in excess of revenues, the expenditure of an additional $3,000,000 – spread over several years – for the purpose of development of the territory to a more nearly self-supporting basis is not unreasonable.

7. By the construction of about 200 miles of new road – in conjunction with about 1,000 miles of new construction in Canada – the territory would gain a physical connection with the vast continental system comprising hundreds of thousands of miles of road in United States, Canada, and Mexico. From the Alaskan or American standpoint, therefore, the advantages are obviously more than commensurate with the cost.

The Commissioners submit the following recommendations:

1. That negotiation be conducted with the Government of Canada, through regular channels, with a view to ascertaining the attitude of Canada with respect to entering into an agreement whereby each Government within its own borders would undertake to survey and locate the best and most practicable route for a highway which would connect the north-western part of the United States with British Columbia, Yukon Territory, and Alaska, prepare specifications and reliable estimates of cost and resulting benefits of said project, and investigate plans for financing the project. The respective organizations should be authorized to communicate directly with each other for the purpose of coordination.

2. That if such agreement be reached, suitable allotments or appropriations should be made available to the Alaska Road Commission for carrying out the purposes of the agreement.

3. That the respective Governments in formulating their road construction programs conform so far as practicable in their own interests to the general route proposed for this highway so that as many as possible of the local projects will be available for and form a part of the main project.

4. That consideration be given by the road-building agencies of Alaska and Yukon Territory to the construction of the Fairbanks-Dawson road without waiting for the adoption of the entire project, in order to develop the intermediate territory and provide an early connection between these two communities, as well as complete a vital link in the proposed through highway.

II. INTRODUCTION

By act of Congress, approved May 15, 1930 (Public No. 228, 71st Cong., H.R. 8368) it was provided:

That the President of the United States is hereby authorized to designate three special commissioners to cooperate with representatives of the Dominion of Canada in a study regarding the construction of a highway to connect the northwestern part of the United States with British Columbia, Yukon Territory, and Alaska, with a view to ascertaining whether such a highway is feasible and economically practicable. Upon completion of such study the results shall be reported to Congress.

The act referred to also authorized the appropriation of $10,000 for carrying out the purposes of the act, and in pursuance of this authority the President appointed as Commissioners to cooperate with representatives of the Dominion of Canada:

Mr. Herbert H. Rice, of Detroit, Michigan, Chairman Mr. Ernest Walker Sawyer, Assistant to the Secretary of the Interior Major Malcolm Elliott, Corps of Engineers, U.S. Army, President, Alaska Road Commission

The appropriation authorized was carried in an act of Congress (Public No. 869, 71st Cong., H.R. 17163) in the following terms:

Study in cooperation with the Dominion of Canada regarding the construction of a highway to connect the United States, British Columbia, Yukon Territory, and Alaska: For the expenses of the United States of a study to be made in cooperation with the Dominion of Canada regarding the construction of a highway to connect the northwestern part of the United States with British Columbia, Yukon Territory, and Alaska, as provided by the Act approved May 15, 1930 (46 Stat., p. 335) including travel and subsistence or per diem in lieu of subsistence (notwithstanding the provisions of any other Act), compensation of employees, stenographic and other services, by contract if deemed necessary without regard to section 3709 of the Revised Statutes (U.S.C. title 41, sec. 5), rent, printing and binding, purchase of supplies and materials and necessary equipment, hire of motor-propelled vehicles, both passenger-carrying and freight-carrying, and such other expenses as may be authorized by the Secretary of State, fiscal years 1931 and 1932, $10,000.

The time for completion was extended by a third act (Public 235, 72d Cong., H.R. 12443) to include the fiscal year 1933.

The members of the Commission met in Washington, D.C., November 7, 1930, organized, and discussed in detail the lines along which the investigation should proceed. Duties were assigned among the members and plans made for securing information necessary for consideration of the project.

An overland route between the United States and Alaska must cross Canadian territory, and a direct route between the State of Washington and the Alaskan boundary would cross British Columbia and, probably, Yukon Territory. It was imperative, therefore, that the Canadian Government, or at least the Provincial Governments concerned, should be approached to ascertain the extent to which those agencies would be willing to cooperate actively in the investigation; or, in the event that active cooperation could not be expected, to secure from them such information as might be available from official and other sources relative to the existing roads, projected works, topographic conditions, and economic development in line with the, subject of the investigation.

The Dominion Government took the position that as the route likely to be selected would lie in either British Columbia or Yukon Territory, or both, the Canadian Government should consider the matter as one of essential interest to the Provinces. With the assent of the Dominion Prime Minister, therefore, representatives of the Provinces were named to act with the Commission.

This report includes the data made available through the cooperation of the Canadian Committee, supplemented by the more detailed knowledge as to the American section of the road furnished by the Alaskan Road Commission.

III. HISTORY OF THE PROJECT

Serious consideration of this project began in 1929. Prior to that time the possibility of such a project being carried through had been mentioned and discussed in a vague way by a number of people but no definite steps were taken toward its accomplishment. In 1929, however, International Highway Associations, formed for the purpose of advocating the project, were formed in Fairbanks, Alaska, and Dawson, Yukon Territory. These associations are still actively engaged in this work. Their mission is to interest the Canadian and American publics in the project and to advocate all necessary legislation and other arrangements for carrying it out. Coincidentally with these events, the Government of British Columbia initiated inquiries on the subject, and informal exchanges of views occurred between that government and officials in Alaska. The project was considered and endorsed by many associations and commercial bodies in Alaska and the United States. Those in Alaska that took such action include: The Chambers of Commerce of Fairbanks, Anchorage, Juneau, Wrangell, Ketchikan, Seward, Sitka, and Nome. The following local associations in the United

States took similar action: Seattle Chamber of Commerce; Western Motor Clubs Conference 1929; Automobile Club of Washington; Seattle Mining Club; and Washington State Good Roads Association. The following national organizations also considered and endorsed the proposal for further study of the project: American Road Builders' Association; National Highways Association; American Automobile Association; and the United States Chamber of Commerce.

The Legislature of Alaska adopted a memorial, April 17, 1929, to the United States Congress endorsing the project and petitioning that steps be taken toward arranging for conferences on the subject between representatives of the United States and Canada. The same body, on May 1, 1929, passed an act providing for the advertisement of the advantages of the project and appropriating funds to be used for that purpose.

The United States Department of the Interior, which maintains general supervision over the Government of Alaska and is greatly interested in the development of the territory, has taken a keen interest in the investigation of the proposed highway. The United States Department of State has conducted conferences, through its representatives, with the Canadian Government and has collected information, maps, etc. The, Alaska Road Commission, which is charged by law with the lay-out, construction, and maintenance of roads in Alaska that are necessary for the development of the territory, has announced that it favors the construction of the Alaska end of the highway whenever the Canadian section of the project is undertaken. This Commission, after preliminary airplane flights over the general area, conducted a survey in 1931 to determine the best route from the Yukon frontier in the vicinity of Dawson to Fairbanks, Alaska. The report of this survey by Mr. Donald MacDonald, locating engineer, appears as appendix E to this report.

The Premier of British Columbia, Honorable Simon Fraser Tolmie, organized and conducted during 1930 an international automobile caravan from Vancouver to Hazelton for the purpose of exploring the northern roads and advocating the extension of the system. The Pacific-Yukon Highway, the name by which the project was designated, was featured on this trip; and it was announced on many occasions that the policy of the Government of British Columbia was in favor of the project, so far as it could be undertaken without interfering with the regular program for expansion of the provincial road system. Accompanying the caravan upon invitation from the Prime Minister of British Columbia were the following Americans: Representatives of various organizations and communities on the Pacific Coast; a representative of the United States Department of the Interior; a representative of the Alaska Road Commission; and representatives of the press. At Hazelton, the northern end of the trip, the caravan party was met by His Honor Randolph Bruce, Lieutenant Governor of British Columbia; Honorable George A. Parks, Governor of Alaska; and representatives from several Alaskan communities.

Airplane and ground reconnaissances were made in 1930 by the Government of British Columbia in the northern part of the Province for the purpose of locating the most favorable route. The results of these surveys and extracts from the reports of the engineers are included in this report. These indicate that a feasible and suitable location was found.

Along with these evidences of interest, there was

the steady and substantial development of a highway system in British Columbia, which included a good gravel surfaced road from Vancouver to Hazelton, a distance of 815 miles. Even prior to the actual appropriation of funds for use of the American Commissioners, but following the act of authorization, it was possible for the members to take part in certain of the activities of the local organizations interested in securing data concerning the project. This circumstance enabled the members to meet many of the local officials in Canada, and to learn of official projects under way in connection with the extension of the road beyond Hazelton. This work consisted of ground and aerial surveys in both British Columbia and Yukon Territory.

A meeting of the members of the Canadian Committee with the American Commissioners was held in Victoria, British Columbia, October 9, 1931, for the purpose of jointly considering the desirability, feasibility, value, route, and cost of the proposed project. The three American Commissioners were present and met with the following Canadian representatives: Honorable George Black of Yukon Territory, Speaker of the Canadian House of Commons; Mr. J. M. Wardle, Chief Engineer, Federal Parks Branch, Canadian Department of Public Works; and Mr. G. P. Napier, Assistant Chief Engineer of the Department of Public Works, British Columbia. Mr. Black was chosen chairman of the joint meeting.

Available data were considered and discussed and a thorough exchange of views was had, as a result of which it was concluded unanimously that the project was feasible from an engineering and constructional standpoint, that substantial benefits would accrue from the project, but that more information was necessary before it could be definitely determined that the project was economically sound.

IV. DESCRIPTION OF THE ROUTE

The Commission has had advantage of excellent cooperation by the Canadian representatives in securing the results of numerous ground and airplane reconnaissance surveys over the present unimproved sections of the route. Several of these have covered areas heretofore uninvestigated for road purposes; and frequently large areas have been included in both ground and air surveys which are today almost wholly wilderness. A road along the rugged coastline of British Columbia and southeastern Alaska broken by glaciers and torrential rivers would obviously be enormously expensive, so consideration of route is limited to the area of more favorable topography east of the coastal mountains.

CLIMATE

The service value of any highway is in some respects affected by seasonal conditions, and it is to be expected that a road reaching so far into the northland might have a somewhat reduced value on account of climatic conditions, and more particularly because of heavy snowfall. Highway maintenance in the United States has, however, clearly demonstrated, both in regions where mountains and where plains prevail, that snow removal or control is entirely feasible to an extent which will enable service to be maintained under practically any conditions prevailing within latitudes falling within the United States.

Consideration of the climatic conditions with special

reference to precipitation and snowfall will indicate the probable open season of a road to Alaska during which a road will be practically unobstructed by snow. Traffic will not, of course, be limited to this season, but it must be recognized that general use of the route by tourists would not extend much beyond the limits of such a favorable period. During the winter months, the ordinary processes of winter maintenance would keep the route still passable for commercial and necessary traffic.

East of the Coast Range throughout British Columbia and northward, the precipitation is comparatively light. In Alaska, at Fairbanks, it is about 11.5 inches; at Dawson in Yukon Territory, about 13 inches. The snowfall in this district varies from 3 to 8 feet, and the snowfall at Dawson is reported to be the heaviest in the Territory. Generally throughout Yukon the precipitation averages about 12.8 inches per year, with a snowfall seldom exceeding 2.5 feet on the level.

In the region around Fairbanks, the normal mean temperature shows a steady rise from 46 F. on May 15 to 60 F. on June 23. This normal mean is maintained until July 27, when it begins to decline, reaching 50°F. on August 31, and 45 F. on September 10.

The climate of the Yukon Territory is of moderate extremes. The winters, though long and cold, are dry and comparatively free of winds. The average day is generally pleasant, permitting outdoor activities during practically the entire season. The summers are delightfully bright and warm. The dryness of the summer season, together with the continuous light, makes it an enjoyable period, and throughout the year the climate is exceptionally healthful.

British Columbia claims the best climate of any of the Canadian Provinces, particularly because it favors outdoor life and industry. The lower mainland region has an average of 36 F. for its coldest month, with a winter mean of 41 F. and a summer mean of 59 F. East of the Coast Range the interior districts are characterized by greater variations in temperature, but have relatively less precipitation, and the low temperatures experienced farther to the east at Edmonton and Winnipeg do not occur in British Columbia.

Throughout the region the hours of sunshine per year range unusually high, with limits from about 1,800 to about 2,200 hours per year. In considering tourist traffic, therefore, a conservative season would extend from April to October, inclusive, five months of which may be expected to be unusually pleasant, with a high percent of sunshine and relatively little rain.

CONNECTION WITH UNITED STATES SYSTEM

The existence in the United States of the system of coordinated Federal-aid highways makes it entirely feasible to effect connection at any point on such system along the Canadian boundary. At Blaine, Washington, a Federal-aid highway, connecting with the entire system in the States, makes connection also with the system of Canadian roads in British Columbia. This point on the international national boundary is indicated, therefore, as the most feasible point of contact between the two countries.

On the United States side the road is improved to a high standard southward to the important cities of the entire Pacific Coast. Northward in British Columbia there is a connecting road westward to the city of Vancouver, British Columbia, the capital of the Province and the metropolis of western Canada.

ROAD TO HAZELTON

From Vancouver the present route to Hazelton follows the Fraser River valley eastward 103 miles to Hope. At this point a general change in the direction of flow of the river causes a turn to the north, and the highway continues, still following the Fraser to Lytton, at mile 176. The route then proceeds up the Thompson and Bonaparte Rivers, following the eastern slope of the watershed to Lac La Hache. Thence it descends the San Jose River to the Fraser at about mile 376. From this point the valley of the Fraser is closely followed to Prince George at the junction of the Fraser and Nechako Rivers, approximately 525 miles from Vancouver. The constructed road then ascends this stream westerly to Fort Fraser and continues in the same general valley northwesterly, here called the Endako, to Hazelton, 830 miles from Vancouver. The present highway continues about 20 miles beyond Hazelton to Kispiox.

HAZELTON, BRITISH COLUMBIA,
TO WHITEHORSE, YUKON TERRITORY

From Hazelton northwestward in the direction of Atlin and Whitehorse the route has been reconnoitered a, distance of approximately 655 miles to the north end of Tagish Lake. For 570 miles the line is in British Columbia and for 85 miles it is in the Yukon Territory. Between Hazelton and the junction of the Klappan and Stikine Rivers, Colonel J. M. Rolston covered three separate routes and several possible alternate combinations, some lines being reconnoitered on the ground, others by plane, and some by a combination of methods. Generally throughout this region the line has been developed over low divides, lightly timbered or partly open country, and sufficiently toward the cast to take advantage of light rainfall, dry ground, and open valleys.

STIKINE RIVER TO YUKON BOUNDARY

The crossing of the Stikine is indicated at some point near the mouth of the Klappan by the several lines reconnoitered from Hazelton.

From the Stikine the line enters a region that is practically continual wilderness to the vicinity of Atlin, and through this section careful studies will be required to locate the best available line. As a result of work so far done by Mr. J. H. Gray, Mr. J. H. McNeil, Colonel J. M. Rolston, and others, control points are established at head of Dease Lake, the Nahlin River, the crossing of the Nakina and Atlin on one line, or as an alternate the head of Dease Lake, the Jennings River, the head of Teslin Lake, Fish Lake, Surprise Lake to Atlin. The former is approximately 251 miles from the Stikine to the boundary of Yukon Territory, as given by Mr. J. H. Gray's careful reconnaissance.

Stikine Crossing to Dease Lake.............50 miles
Dease Lake to Nahlin River................80 miles
Nahlin River to Atlin....................91 miles
Atlin to Yukon boundary..................30 miles

Total...............................251 miles

As shown by Mr. J. H. McNeil, following the airplane reconnaissance of Colonel J. M. Rolston, the mileage is approximately as follows:

Stikine Crossing to Dease Lake.............46 miles
Dease Lake to Teslin Lake................137 miles
Teslin Lake to foot of Surprise Lake.........80 miles
Surprise Lake to Atlin....................11 miles
Atlin to Yukon boundary..................30 miles

Total...............................304 miles

The route via Teslin Lake keeps to the east and at the expense of greater mileage has the advantage of dryer ground and less precipitation. It is the preferred route of Mr. McNeil and Colonel Rolston. It was apparently not studied beyond Dease Lake by Mr. Gray who made a ground reconnaissance of the Nahlin River route.

YUKON BOUNDARY TO ALASKA

Through this territory the routes explored offered less difficulty as the area is less broken and the existing trails, from the head of the White Pass and Yukon Railway, at Whitehorse to Dawson, have been in greater use than those south of Atlin. Mr. J. H. McNeil, Superintendent of Highways of Yukon Territory, supplied the information for this section and developed a line apparently closely following the preferred trail from the southern Provincial boundary to Dawson on the Klondike.

This follows the lake about 22 miles to Carcross and thence closely parallels the railroad to Whitehorse, a distance of approximately 43 miles, making a total of 110 miles in Yukon and 1,510 miles from Vancouver. The line then proceeds up the Takhini River to Little River and up that stream to the Yukon River divide, which is crossed near Kynocks. Thence the route continues down the Klusha River and the Nordenskild to Carmacks, 1,643 miles from Vancouver. From Carmacks to Minto the route is along the Lewes River (a name given to the upper reaches of the Yukon), which is crossed at mile 1,663 at Yukon Crossing. At Minto the reconnoitered line diverges to the northward, crossing the divide to the Stewart River (1,773 miles) which is then followed for about 35 miles, where the valley is again left to climb the comparatively low Klondike divide. The Klondike River is reached at a point near Glenboyle, 1,856 miles from Vancouver, and this stream is followed to Dawson, mile 1,865, at the junction with the Yukon River. From Dawson the remaining 65 miles to the Alaskan boundary are along a ridge location to a point near Walker Fork where the reconnaissance of the Alaska Road Commission ties in with the route.

In Alaska, the reconnoitered line will probably ascend some favorable branch of Fortymile River and crossing the divide at an elevation of about 3,500 feet descend the Tanana River to McCarty (Grundler), a distance of 183 miles in Alaska. At McCarty junction will be made with the Richardson Highway, 91 miles from Fairbanks.

The total approximate distance from Vancouver to Dawson is 1,865 miles; to the Alaska line, 1,930 miles; to McCarty, 2,113 miles; and to Fairbanks, 2,204 miles. From Whitehorse to Fairbanks via Dawson the total distance is 694 miles, of which 573 miles remain to be built and 31 miles to be surf aced and otherwise improved.

ALTERNATE ROUTES FROM WHITEHORSE
TO ALASKA

From the point of view of best serving Canadian interests, there is no alternate route to that shown on the maps accompanying this report via Whitehorse and Dawson. But from Alaska, it is possible to develop two alternate routes, either of which would serve Fairbanks and the interior equally well. From Fairbanks a route following the Tanana River practically to its headwaters would shorten the distance to Whitehorse and would decrease total required new construction by about 100 miles. This route would leave the Richardson Highway at McCarty, as in the case of the preferred route to Dawson. A second alternate leaves the Richardson Highway at Gulkana and extends practically due east to Kluane Lake via the headwaters of the White River and thence to Whitehorse.

The Tanana River route also via Kluane Lake, is about 650 miles long from Fairbanks to Whitehorse, and, of this, 350 miles are in Alaska and 300 in Yukon. Of the 350 miles in Alaska, 90 miles are already complete in the section of the Richardson Highway between Fairbanks and McCarty. The remaining 260 miles would have to be built. In Yukon Territory about 150 miles have been graded, leaving for construction about 150 miles. The total new construction required on this route is 360 miles of complete road and, in addition, 150 miles of improvement and surfacing.

The total length from Fairbanks to Whitehorse by Gulkana and Kluane Lake is about 724 miles, and the constructed section along the Richardson Highway in Alaska involved in this route is 240 miles in length. Of the balance to Kluane Lake (334 miles), the section between Gulkana and Chisana (154 miles) – all in Alaska – is under construction, leaving 180 miles to be built, of which 50 miles will be in Alaska and 130 miles in Yukon Territory. The road between Kluane Lake and Whitehorse will need extensive improvements and surfacing.

The following table compares these various routes from Whitehorse to Fairbanks:

Whitehorse to Fairbanks via –	Total length	On Richardson Highway (completed)	Other sections (completed or projected)	To be surfaced	To be entirely constructed
	Miles	Miles	Miles	Miles	Miles
Dawson	694	90	0	31	573
Kluane Lake-McCarty	650	90	0	150	500
Kluane Lake-Gulkana	724	240	154	150	180

Although from this comparison it appears that the Gulkana route would equally well serve Fairbanks and would require the least new construction in both Yukon and Alaska, its adoption would be at the expense of Dawson and the needed road between that place and Whitehorse.

PRESENT GENERAL CONDITION

From Vancouver and Blaine the present road to Hazelton, known as far as Prince George as the Caribou Highway, is constructed with a gravel surface. All bridges are in and the road is available for use throughout the year. The surface is of ample width, having easy grades and curves, and is well maintained. At Yale, which is head of navigation on the Fraser, the road enters the picturesque Fraser River Canyon which extends to Lytton, a distance of 59 miles. The road is benched along the canyon wall and where necessary is protected along the outer edge by a stone guard wall. The total improved distance to Hazelton is 830 miles.

From Discovery to Atlin (11 miles) and for 10 miles beyond the road had been opened for motor travel (21 miles).

From Robinson, a station on the White Pass and Yukon Railroad, about 20 miles south of Whitehorse, a graded wagon road exists to Whitehorse and beyond to Minto, a total distance of about 196 miles. The low grade road from Whitehorse to Kluane Lake, previously mentioned, is passable only in good weather but could be improved to suitable standard at reasonable cost. The length of this branch is about 150 miles.

In Alaska the Richardson and Steese Highways together form a link connecting the north Pacific Coast port of Valdez with the upper Yukon River at Circle. The Richardson Highway extends from Valdez to Fairbanks, 371 miles, and the Steese Highway from Fairbanks to Circle, 160 miles. This main axis has several branches, the aggregate length of the system being about 900 miles. South of Fairbanks, 91 miles, is McCarty, at which point the Whitehorse-Dawson-Fairbanks route would connect with the Richardson Highway system. About 240 miles south of Fairbanks the branch road connecting with Chisana turns eastwardly from Gulkana and would be a part of the Whitehorse-Kluane Lake-Gulkana-Fairbanks route. The Alaska roads to which the international project would give access are generally of fair gravel-surface standard. They are passable during the open season at all times except in a few spots where destructive freshets and slides sometimes carry away bridges or short sections of road, necessitating the occasional employment of tractors for assisting vehicles over critical places.

In British Columbia, north of Hazelton there would probably be considerable difficulty in keeping roads open during the winter months especially in the mountainous sections. In the upland valleys less difficulty would be experienced. In Yukon Territory and central Alaska roads could be maintained in usable condition for automotive vehicles for about seven months of year – June to December – with only a moderate amount of snow removal. Tractor and horse-drawn sleds could generally use the roads all winter.

Summarizing the extent of the existing road system in the Canadian Provinces and Alaska applicable to the proposed project, it is seen that the total constructed grade from Seattle to Fairbanks by the Dawson route is about 1,073 miles, of which about 970 miles are surfaced with gravel. The rest of the distance, 1,183 miles, remains to be constructed. Of this, 196 miles are graded at least in part, and in Yukon Territory along the existing trail, there have already been constructed many bridges that are of a capacity to carry tractors and heavy vehicles. By the Kluane Lake-Gulkana route about 1,296 miles have been constructed or are under construction; 200 miles of reconstruction or improvement; and about 790 miles of new construction would be needed.

A more detailed description of the route from Vancouver to Hazelton appears in appendix A.

Hazelton is the possible point of departure for overland travel to the north. The most favorable route for a highway through this little-known country is still to be determined, but sufficient explorations have been made by airplane and otherwise to ascertain that there are practicable locations which will involve no insuperable or unusual difficulty.

The known resources along the route are: Copper, silver, and gold in the vicinity of Stewart, British Columbia; coal in the Groundhog section about 140 miles north of Hazelton and eastwardly thereof; gold in the Stikine River area (near Telegraph Creek); gold in the Taku River area Northeast of Juneau; gold, silver, and lead in the Atlin area; and furs and timber at many places along the entire route.

There is no overland route – other than trails – connecting these areas. They are reached individually by way of the rivers which cut through the Coast Range and discharge into the waters of southeastern Alaska. The rivers are swift, shallow in many places, and dangerous. Navigation on them is beset with many difficulties.

Atlin is a community of several hundred people whose activities consist of mining, prospecting, trapping, trading, agriculture for local supply, and fur farming. Mining is being conducted on a fairly large scale.

Access to this region is obtained over the White Pass and Yukon Railroad to Carcross, thence by boats operating on the lakes. Large numbers of tourists come each year over this route to enjoy the scenery and climate. Comfortable accommodations are found, and the train and boat service are excellent.

This lake region around Atlin is on the divide separating the Pacific Coast drainage from that of the Yukon River system, which flows over 2,000 miles into Bering Sea. Just east of Atlin is the crest of the Cassiar Mountains which at this point is the dividing line between the Pacific Ocean and Arctic Ocean drainage.

There are short roads leading in various directions from Atlin to connect with nearby areas. One of these – the road south to O'Donnel River, 25 miles, is favorably situated to be included in the Pacific-Yukon project. It is a fair country road, easily traveled in good weather.

Reconnaissance from Hazelton was made by Colonel Rolston and Mr. Gray, and extracts from their reports are included in appendices B and C.

These investigations covered three routes as far as the junction of the Stikine and Klappan Rivers, and alternate routes beyond the Stikine to Atlin on the lake of that name.

From Atlin a reconnaissance was made by Mr. J. H. McNeil, Superintendent of Works and Buildings of Yukon Territory, and extracts from the McNeil report appear in appendix D.

Whitehorse and Dawson are the two principal towns of Yukon Territory and are connected by the Yukon River, navigable about four months of the year, and a winter sled road which accommodates travel during the winter. A regular stage service is maintained all winter. During critical periods such as the break-up in early summer, there is no overland communication, as the ice, both on the river and road, is too soft to support traffic. Parts of the road will sustain traffic in dry weather during the summer months.

River traffic is cared for by steamboats of the stern-wheel type. They have good passenger accommodations. A large number of tourists go over this route each year. The downstream trip from Whitehorse to Dawson requires about 36 hours; the upstream trip, 4½ days. Whitehorse is the head of navigation of the Yukon system. This great waterway runs northwest, through Yukon Territory and continues westward through Alaska to Bering Sea. It is navigable during the open summer months throughout its 2,000 miles of length. The head of the river at Whitehorse is reached from Skagway,

Alaska, by the White Pass and Yukon Railroad, 111 miles long.

So far as known, the topography and soil conditions in Yukon Territory are such that road building would not be difficult or expensive. The chief obstacles would be the river crossings—Yukon, Pelly, and Stewart; since all of these rivers are navigable, ferries could be employed until such time as traffic demands bridges.

Yukon Territory has an area of 207,000 square miles and though possessed of great resources is only scantily populated, the total population being not over 6,000 people—about one person for every 35 square miles. During the Klondike boom days there was a population of probably 30,000. With the exhaustion of the diggings that could be worked by hand or crude appliances, a large part of this population disappeared from the Territory. In these days under modern production methods, a few men do the work that required hundreds a generation ago.

The mineral resources still remaining in large quantities consist of gold, silver, copper, lead, antimony, tungsten, and iron, besides coal and other nonmetallic substances. The principal camps now under development are Carmacks, Kluane Lake, Dawson (Klondike), and Mayo. The production from the Dawson area is now running about $750,000 per year.

The valleys, hillsides and lower plateaus of the Yukon carry a good forest growth—white spruce, balsam fir, jack pine, cottonwood, poplar, and birch.

There is water power in abundance. Some development to meet the requirements of the mining industry has occurred.

Farm products include wheat, oats, barley, and hay. Garden products grow well—potatoes, carrots, beets, turnips, parsnips, cauliflower, cabbage, celery, strawberries, currants, etc.

The native fur-bearers are weasel, muskrat, lynx, wolverine, bear, otter, marten, mink, red fox, white fox, cross fox, silver fox, wolf, coyote and beaver. This has been a favorite trapping ground for over a hundred years. The raising of fur-bearers in captivity—fox and mink especially—has been profitable, and, the possibilities for expansion in this activity are almost without limit.

The scenic attractions of Yukon Territory now draw hundreds of tourists every year. Thousands more would be able to enjoy this trip were there a road over which they could travel. During May, June, July, and August, there is practically no darkness, and though the sun is not visible at midnight until Fort Yukon, Alaska, is reached, its reflected light is seen in the sky all night, producing displays of color beyond description. The summer weather is generally fair, the average precipitation being but 12 inches per year. Residents and tourists alike enjoy the cool agreeable summers.

The general route from Dawson to Fairbanks is in a westerly direction and will probably ascend Fortymile Creek and, surmounting a divide at an elevation of about 3,500 feet above sea level, descend into the Tanana River valley to a junction with the Richardson Highway at McCarty (where Richardson Highway crosses the Tanana River). There is now a winter sled road from Dawson toward Chicken Creek, Alaska, which would need considerable improvement including some relocation to serve as a summer road. United States Geological

Survey contour maps of the region between the Tanana and Yukon Rivers and reports of prospectors, trappers, and aviators who have seen the country, indicate that road building will not be unusually difficult. From the junction with the Richardson Highway at McCarty, the route will follow a good motor road 91 miles to Fairbanks. This road is open usually about six months—between June and December. It could be kept open all winter with relatively little work of snow removal if traffic volume should demand.

The section of the proposed road west of Dawson taps the Eagle-Chicken Creek gold mining area which has been a consistent producer for many years, and there is no evidence of approaching exhaustion of the mineral resources. United States Geological Survey engineers who have inspected this region are of the opinion that further prospecting is justified. The existing wagon road south from Eagle could be extended to connect with the Pacific-Yukon Highway and would then be of service in connecting this highway with the Seventymile section which is along the south side of Yukon between Eagle and Circle.

All of the country touched by the proposed highway, between the Yukon border and the junction with the Richardson Highway, is favorable for trapping of wild fur-bearers. Caribou and moose are found. There are many areas capable of cultivation. Serviceable timber occurs in the valleys. The population is very scant as the whole region has been and is now quite inaccessible.

A continuation of the route in Alaska was reconnoitered by Mr. Donald MacDonald, Locating Engineer of the Alaska Road Commission. The report is included in appendix E.

Desperate to promote the concept of an International Highway from Fairbanks to the lower 48 states, boosters from Fairbanks persuaded Slim Williams and a young companion, John Logan, to ride used custom-built, rigid-framed, lightweight BSA motorcycles cross-country to test the route. The adventurers took seven months to ride the 2,300 miles from Fairbanks to Chicken, Alaska; Dawson and Whitehorse, Yukon; Atlin, Telegraph Creek and Hazelton, British Columbia; to Seattle, Washington. Logan's BSA motorcycle is on display at the University of Alaska Museum in Fairbanks.
UNIVERSITY OF ALASKA MUSEUM

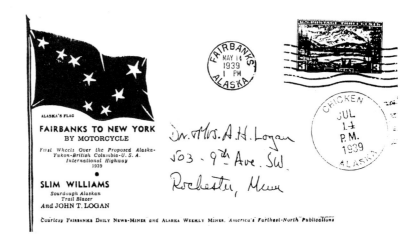

2
NORTHWEST STAGING ROUTE

Military aircraft at the Edmonton, Alberta, Municipal Airport, June 1942. The P-39 fighters are destined for the Russian front. YA A5300

Alaskan and Canadian Defenses

After the purchase of Alaska from Russia in 1867, various military units were stationed in the southeast section for years. Gold was discovered in the Juneau area in the 1880s and more strikes were made in the Klondike in 1896, at Nome in 1899 and in Fairbanks in the early 1900s. The need for more civil and military presence was apparent. Troops were stationed at several military posts in Alaska including Chilkoot Barracks at Haines. Other units went into the interior to set up a communications system.

By 1940 there were over 72,000 people in Alaska and it was apparent that not only was Alaska a vital gateway to Canada and the west coast of the United States but its defenses were sorely lacking. Russia was reported to be building an air base on Big Diomede Island only one and one-half miles from Alaska and the infamous Gen. Billy Mitchell had warned for years of a possible Japanese attack. The first major contingent of American troops arrived at Anchorage in the spring of 1940 and a submarine and air base were built at Sitka in southeastern Alaska along with air bases at Fairbanks, Anchorage and Kodiak. The naval base at Dutch Harbor in the Aleutian Islands was strengthened.

After the fall of France in June 1940, the United States and Canada set up a Canadian-American Permanent Joint Board of Defense in August to oversee all defense policies for both countries. This included approving the Northwest Staging Route air bases and the Alaska Highway.

The Japanese were greatly disturbed by the American defense moves as shown in a newspaper article in 1941.

Japan Greatly Disturbed Over Proposed Highway To Alaska From United States

The newspaper *Hochi* stated today that Japan is greatly disturbed over reported plans for building a military highway from the United States to Alaska through western Canada. The newspaper said that the Tokyo foreign office was informed that a string of air bases will be built along the highway by the United States and Canadian governments.

Hochi declared "American measures in this direction will be regarded as a continuation of the horseshoe-shaped encirclement of Japan by the Washington Government. Military bases of the United States would thus be strategic from Singapore via Australia, the Philippines, Hawaii and the United States to Canada and Alaska."

Even with this increased military activity, Alaska was open to surprise attack as the United States was drawn into the war in December 1941.

Northwest Staging Route

With the beginning of the Second World War in September 1939 Canada began to look at its own defense posture. The defense of western Canada, and to a degree Alaska and the western United States, was the main reason a string of air bases extending from Edmonton, Alberta, to Fairbanks, Alaska, was proposed to be built. The purpose of those bases was to facilitate the movement of aircraft and supplies to western Canada and Alaska. In early 1941, bases were constructed in Grande Prairie, Alberta; Fort Nelson, British Columbia; and Watson Lake and Whitehorse, Yukon Territory. The existing Ladd Field at Fairbanks, Alaska, was expanded and the northern terminus of the air route. Bases were also built at Prince George and Smithers, British Columbia.

This air route followed one pioneered by Grant McConachie and his Yukon Southern Air Transport in the 1930s.

The Northwest Staging Route, as it was to become known, had two very important functions during the war. First, it not only was the main factor in locating the highway along the present route, but it was very useful in the highway construction. Second, the airfields were used a great deal by American pilots ferrying planes to Fairbanks to be picked up by Russian crews for Lend-Lease to Russia.

P-40 fighter planes lined up at the Fort Nelson airfield in April 1942. These planes were bound for the 11th Air Force in Alaska. In addition, thousands of Lend-Lease aircraft bound for Russia passed through the Northwest Staging Route airfields between 1942 and 1945. USA SC 322879

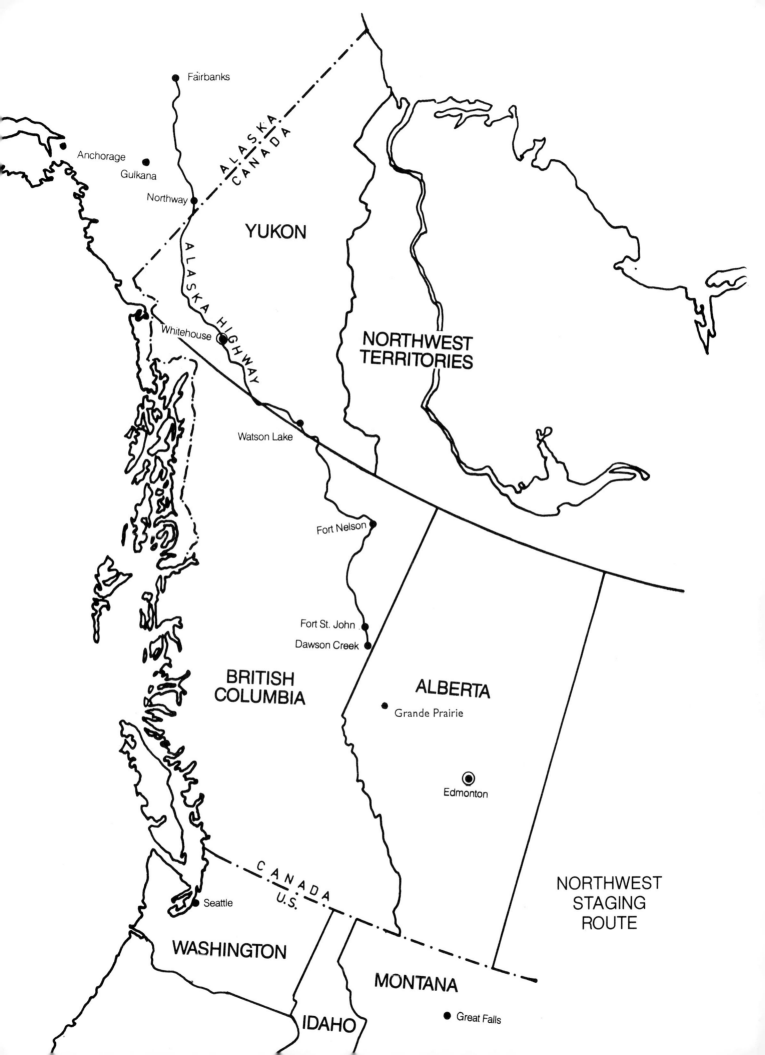

East Base at Great Falls, Montana, was the southernmost airfield of the Northwest Staging Route and the staging field for the thousands of aircraft heading north. 11TH AIR FORCE

Airfield at Grande Prairie, Alberta. 11TH AIR FORCE

Airfield at Fort St. John, B.C. 11TH AIR FORCE

Airfield at Fort Nelson, B.C. 11TH AIR FORCE

Airfield at Watson Lake, Yukon. 11TH AIR FORCE

Airfield at Whitehorse, Yukon, built on a bluff above the town. 11TH AIR FORCE

The Northway Alaska airfield, an intermediate stop between Whitehorse and Fairbanks. 11TH AIR FORCE

Ladd Field in Fairbanks, Alaska, the northern terminus of the Northwest Staging Route and a transfer point for planes of the Russian Lend-Lease program. RANDY ACCORD

Lend-Lease planes destined for Russia on a Northwest Staging Route airfield. 11TH AIR FORCE

Two B-24 heavy bombers.

A B-26 medium bomber.

A C-60 Loadstar.

A P-39 fighter.

All photos were taken at the Fort St. John airfield.
DAVE SIMPSON

3

THE TOTE ROAD

An engineer chopping through the permanently frozen soil that was present along the road route. Road building of this magnitude had never before been attempted in this country and it took quite a while to figure out how to deal with the unusual soil conditions. NA 30-N-43-340

THE NOME NUGGET

Published Monday, Wednesday, Friday, by The Nome
Publishing Company, Nome, Alaska.

Telephone Main 114   P. O. Box 518

Entered in the Post Office in Nome as 2nd Class Matter

Subscription Rates Payable In Advance

Delivered by carrier in Nome and Little Creek for $2.00 per month
By mail, postage paid, outside of Nome & vicinity $1.50 per month.

MEMBER OF ASSOCIATED PRESS

Alaska Highway Is War Project

THOROUGHFARE FROM EDMONTON WILL HELP DEVELOPMENT WHEN PEACE COMES

By SAM JACKSON

SEATTLE, June 1 —In Canada some 30,000 men are desperately pushing a road—the only road—connecting the United States with its vast, rich and supremely strategic territory of Alaska. Like many other things, the Alaska highway looks much different since Pearl Harbor than it looked before. When I visited Alaska it was almost incredible to a newcomer that the road had not already been built. Shipping already was badly strained; so was airplane traffic.

No Auto or Rail Road

Yet neither auto road nor rail road ran, or yet runs, between the war plants of the home country and our military dispositions—defensive and offensive— which are nearest Japan.

Cost estimates were mild as road-building goes — from $14,000,000 to $50,000,000, with most estimates running around $30,000,000. But Canada didn't want to pay for a road that was essentially a United States war measure, and Uncle Sam didn't want to pay for a line of British Columbia filling stations, pubs, auto courts and improved transportation for Canadian lumberjacks and miners.

Path Across Wilderness

The new road cuts a bold path across the wilderness from Edmonton, Alberta, the "jumping off place" in the westernmost of Canada's prairie provinces, to Fairbanks. In a territory that compares in size with the Mississippi Valley, Fairbanks is the metropolis of inland Alaska.

With a war on, Uncle Sam is now paying for the road and liking it. After the war, Canada is supposed to take over maintenance. As for the new road, west coast civic organizations were disappointed that it did not continue an existing route leading through Seattle and Vancouver to the little farming village of Hazelton, 612 miles north of the border.

Traffic Goes By Sea Chiefly

The highway will carry the motorist, when peace and tires allow, into an unexploited land of beauty — through what one poet called "deep, death-like valleys" screened by "big dizzy mountains." Here abound moose, bighorn, marten, fox, mink and beaver. Growing wild are cranberries, blueberries, mushrooms, fields of roses. The climate, varying from summer's 90 degrees to winter's 68 below is not unbearable because the atmosphere is dry, piercing winds, rare. Summer nights are cool in the Land of the Northern Lights.

Old Fur Trail

From Fort St. John, British Columbia, the road will follow an old fur trail north to Fort Nelson Airport. Along the way stretch unplowed lands of rich soil. To the northwest it will cross, perhaps follow, the Laird river, tributary of the Arctic-bound MacKenzie. Flowing in from the south is Trout river, enticing fishermen. Devil's Portage means a weary walk-and-carry. Farther downstream is the 40-mile Grand Canyon of the Laird, with its Rapid of the Drowned Hell Gate marks the end of dangerous navigation.

Valleys Green All Winter

North of the Laird lie verdant valleys, whose hot springs are said to keep them green all winter

Swinging into Yukon Territory, the highway will go to Watson Lake. Westward to Whitehorse, it will bisect a famed 1898 trail along which gold seekers struggled to the Klondike. As the road continues north west it will pass loftly mountains, glaciers, until it winds up at Fairbanks, the door to Asia.

Lt. Gen. Brehon Burke Somervell, chief of the Army's Services of Supply (S.O.S.), was responsible for getting the needed supplies to the North Country for construction of the highway and pipeline projects. NA III-SC-126338

First Troops to Dawson Creek

Members of the 341st Engineers stake out tent sites at their bivouac area at Dawson Creek, B.C. in May 1942. USA

U.S. Army Headquarters at Dawson Creek, 1942.
MILT BRUNSON COLLECTION

Troops disembark from rail cars of the Northern Alberta Railroad at Dawson Creek. MILT BRUNSON COLLECTION

Road construction equipment by the hundreds rolled into Dawson Creek by rail in the spring of 1942. LC-USW33-943-ZC

Horsepower was used early in the highway survey to get teams out in the bush to locate the centerline. Local packers and natives who knew the area were hired to help the surveyors determine the best route to follow. USA SC 323260, GA NA-1854-2, YA 77/10 U.S. ARMY PHOTO

Sometimes the only thing that could get through the country was horsepower and even this was difficult at times.

NA 30-N-43-3357

When United States Army Engineer troops reached Dawson Creek and Whitehorse in the spring of 1942 they faced a formidable task. They had to construct sixteen hundred miles of military highway, most of it through unsurveyed territory, across rivers whose courses had not been traced and mountains where no passes had been explored. And they had to complete the road before the Japanese could secure a foothold in Alaska. Some said they would do well to finish the survey in 1942. Others asserted that the muskeg would prove impossible.

Despite the bitter controversy created by the selection of the route after the American and Canadian commissions had recommended one or the other of the two coastal routes, once the decision to build the highway was made, no time was lost. On February 4, 1942, Brig. Gen. C.L. Sturdevant, United States Army Assistant Chief of Engineers, was instructed to prepare surveys and plans. On February 14 he received authority to proceed with construction of the highway. Five days later United States Army officers were conferring in Edmonton with James MacArthur, general manager of the Northern Alberta Railways, on arrangements for transporting equipment to Dawson Creek. On February 26 the agreement between Canada and the United States was signed. By March equipment was being moved over the Northern Alberta Railways line to Dawson Creek and from Skagway over the White Pass and Yukon Railway to Carcross and Whitehorse. On March 10 the first troops arrived at Dawson Creek.

Brig. Gen. William M. Hoge set up his headquarters at Whitehorse with two regiments, the 18th and 340th, and one black regiment, the 93rd, to begin construction of the northern end of the highway. At the same time, two other regiments, the 35th and the 341st, and one black regiment, the 95th, began work on the southern end of the highway out of Fort St. John, where Brig. Gen. J.A. O'Connor, then a colonel, had established his headquarters. With ancillary troops, some ten thousand officers and men were engaged on the greatest engineering project in the Americas since the completion of the Panama Canal in 1913.

At the northern end, the 18th Regiment reached Whitehorse on April 29. The 93rd and 340th regiments remained in Skagway to wait for their equipment until June. Then the 93rd moved to Carcross to start building the highway between that town and Teslin Lake and the 340th went to Teslin Lake to begin work on the road south to Watson Lake. In June, also, another black regiment, the 97th, was moved from Valdez, Alaska, over the Richardson Highway to Slana. There it started work on the Alaskan end of the highway while the 18th Regiment built the road through the Yukon north of Whitehorse.

At the southern end, the 35th Regiment was the first to reach Dawson Creek and it proceeded immediately with its equipment over the winter trail to Fort Nelson to begin work out of there on the road to Watson Lake. At the end of April the 341st Regiment arrived at Dawson Creek to work on the highway between Fort St. John and Fort Nelson. The third regiment, the 95th, reached Dawson Creek in June and followed the 341st and 35th regiments, improving the pioneer road, putting in culverts and building bridges.

The one reason the Engineers were able to build the highway in one season, confounding all those who claimed it could not be done, lay in the achievement of the 35th Regiment in getting to Fort Nelson with all its heavy roadbuilding machinery before the breakup. There was no road to Fort Nelson, 325 miles north of Dawson Creek. The road, such as it was, ended at Fort St. John. From there a winter trail, impassable after the thaw, ran to Fort Nelson, 265 miles away. Over this little-used trail the 35th had to take all its equipment, including twenty heavy diesel tractors and bulldozers, in temperatures falling sometimes to forty-five degrees below zero. It had to cross the Peace River on a plank road covered with sawdust built over the ice. But by April 5 the last of its tractors, trucks and graders had been taken to Fort Nelson.

Even then the problem of supplying the regiment remained. When it ran short of fuel before the highway from Fort St. John was finished, a shipment of fuel oil had to be sent by rail to Waterways and by river and lake boats down the Clearwater and Athabaska rivers, across Great Slave Lake and down the Mackenzie River to Fort Simpson. From there it was sent up the Liard and Fort Nelson rivers to Fort Nelson, in all a distance of some 1,100 miles from the railhead at Waterways as compared to the 325 miles from the railhead at Dawson Creek.

While bulldozers were already starting to cut a swath through the bush, a stereoscopic examination of overlapping aerial photographs revealed a route over the mountain unknown to any of the trappers and prospectors or the Indians. At first, after a study of the best maps of the territory available, the Engineers had thought that from Watson Lake the highway would have to swing south around Dease Lake, Telegraph Creek and Atlin to reach Whitehorse. This would have added nearly five hundred miles to its length. But this new direct route from Watson Lake to Teslin Lake was entirely in forest growth and in these latitudes forest growth does not thrive higher than four thousand feet.

"By knowing our trees we were able to follow the high ridges and avoid many of the muskeg areas," Colonel Albert E. Lane, the commanding officer at the Dawson Creek railhead, explained to me. "We studied the aerial stereopair photographs of the country and picked out the ridges of poplar and jack pine indicating the higher ground.

"Part of the route we selected for the road was unknown even to the Indians. When the 35th Regiment reached the head of the Tetsa River the Indians shook their heads after they heard about the route we proposed to follow from that point. 'White man's way, two summers. Indian's way, one summer,' they said. They thought we should follow their trails. So we sent a party out with Indian guides to survey the route they suggested. They were gone all summer and they still had not reached their destination when we brought them out. In the meantime, the highway had been built."

Ahead of the construction crews went the surveyors, presently so short a distance ahead that the bulldozers caught up to them while they slept.

Between Fort St. John and Fort Nelson and as far as Steamboat Mountain beyond Fort Nelson the muskeg presented the Engineers with one of their most difficult construction problems. By following the higher ground to the west of the old winter trail to Fort Nelson they could avoid most of the muskeg. But at times there was no way around it. They crossed it by using corduroy, which is simply a roadbed of logs laid on top of the swamp and covered with earth. Sometimes they built their road and it sank slowly into the spongy bog of moss, peat and silt as the muskeg thawed. Then they had to put a second layer of corduroy on top of the first and perhaps still more layers until they obtained a firm foundation for the road. On one stretch fifty miles from Fort Nelson the 35th Regiment had to build two miles of corduroy road.

Mud was another problem. The 35th Regiment made little progress for weeks after it reached Fort Nelson because the heavy rains turned the ground into a quagmire. At Charlie Lake, where the 341st Regiment was starting on the highway north from Fort St. John, vehicles bogged down in the mud and construction work was brought to a standstill. Men and equipment were ferried up the lake to begin building on the higher ground at the north end. This effort to avoid a delay of weeks when every day was precious cost the lives of twelve men. A pontoon boat ferry carrying two officers and fifteen men capsized in a sudden squall. Dressed in their heavy winter clothing the men had little chance to swim in the icy waters of the lake and the officers and ten of the men were drowned. The other five soldiers were rescued by Gus Hedin, a trapper, who witnessed the accident and put out his skiff to pick them up.

They were not the only soldiers and civilians to give their lives. Several men were killed in accidents caused by bad fills giving way. Others froze to death before they were found. A few died from carbon monoxide gas poisoning while sitting in the cabs of their stalled trucks waiting for assistance. But the highway was built.

U.S. ARMY UNITS THAT CONSTRUCTED
THE ORIGINAL TOTE ROAD, 1942

18th Engineer Combat Regiment
35th Engineer Combat Regiment
93rd Engineer General Service Regiment (cld)
95th Engineer General Service Regiment (cld)
97th Engineer General Service Regiment (cld)
340th Engineer General Service Regiment
341st Engineer General Service Regiment
Co. D, 29th Engineer Topographic Battalion
Co. A, 648th Engineer Topographic Battalion
73rd Engineer Light Pontoon Company
74th Engineer Light Pontoon Company

Brig. Gen. Clarence L. Sturdevant, assistant chief of engineers, was responsible for the overall construction project. ASL PCA 175-128

The advance survey parties set up bases along the proposed highway route. This is a cook tent for the officers' mess near Carcross, Yukon in July 1942. USA SC 322932

Members of the 341st Engineers survey the route between Fort St. John and Fort Nelson in May 1942. Surveying through the dense forest was difficult but necessary to lay out a line for the bulldozers to follow. The centerline was roughed on maps, but the line had to be surveyed and investigated on the ground. USA SC 322893

Transit crew in the Yukon, 1942. BILL HEBERT COLLECTION

Plane table survey work continued all along the highway route until the centerline was firmly established.
NA 208-LU-24-G-5

U.S. Army officers stand in front of Headquarters, Whitehorse Sector, Alcan Highway, in June 1942. USA SC 322908

Territorial Gov. Ernest Gruening of Alaska, second from left, visited the Public Roads Administration camp in October 1942. On the left is Brig. Gen. James D. O'Connor, commanding general of the construction project. Third from left is Col. John Wheeler, in charge of the actual construction and next to him is Col. K. Bush, Chief of Staff. NA 30-N-43-1441

The Eighteenth Engineers Regiment in Yukon Territory

The following description was written by Fred Rust, the historian of the 18th Engineers. It is typical of the life the soldiers endured during the initial phase of construction from April 1942 to January 1943.

Each full company camp was a complete community under canvas with orderly room, kitchen, supply, PX, shower, laundry and barber (usually a farmer). The platoon camp often lacked all but the kitchen and depended on occasional visits of the PX man and barber. Camps were hastily erected in or near woods and close to water, tents dispersed informally, their ropes made fast to the handiest trees. The charming ditch latrine was standard, "improved" if time allowed. Frequent inspections by medical officers insured the maintenance of sanitation, but bivouacs were not painfully neat with the exception of those of "E," which always looked as though a four-star general was expected. The average looked like what it was, the temporary dwelling of men who had a job to do.

We struck camp, moved and pitched camp one day, were at work the next. We built and bulldozed twenty-four hours a day, seven days a week. We lived dirty, we grew beards.

Tents averaging seven occupants were overcrowded for men who carried two full barracks bags and the usual gear, plus sleeping bag. Soldiers are fiends for building private boxes. We slept without pillows on canvas cots without mattresses, in which condition the cot has about the same "give" as a concrete floor. We jammed what gear we could under our bunks, the rest we hung in the air. A soldier's closet is the air and our tents were full of strings, ropes and miscellaneous rigging holding clothes, rifles, anything we wanted to keep off the ground. We found a place to hang a picture of the "girl at home", or pin-ups. The stove dried the ground until the floor was deep dust.

Each shelter contained a Wheeling stove, much better than the old Sibley. It took a terrible beating in the number of times pitched, folded and transported. When we put up some of these well-worn tents at Adak the following year, they survived a williwaw that ripped a later issue from top to bottom. Our summer costume was blue fatigues, boots or shoes and the World War I campaign hat, but you can give a thousand soldiers the same fatigue uniform and they will all manage to look different, especially in regard to hats. The degree and kind of our raggedness made us look different too; whether our clothes were plastered with grease or pine pitch, and where they were torn.

In one respect discipline was never relaxed. Rifle inspections were regularly held. Between checks we protected our pieces by wrapping them in mattress covers or with two arctic socks pulled over the butt and muzzle ends. Ordnance at Kodiak later said the 18th's rifles were the best they'd checked.

In full-company camps a shower was set up. This was improvised by erecting a tower to support two or three steel gasoline drums, for water storage. A homemade coil in a Wheeling stove, beneath the tower, heated water thermally and gravity carried it to shower nozzles in the bath tent. Company laundrymen filled the drums with power pumps when available, otherwise with block, tackle, pail and muscle. These men fed the stove and used surplus shower water for laundering our clothes, a service for which we gladly paid. The gasoline driven Montgomery Ward washing machines, purchased by company funds at Vancouver, held up well in the Yukon, were later rebuilt.

In the smaller camps we took pail-baths, eventually developing skillful, acrobatic bathing techniques. We also washed our own clothes, after a fashion. We could get clean but we couldn't stay clean.

The roof of our mess halls was the sky. In the summer we scattered around on the ground and in the winter we tried to get to a tent before our food froze. Generally, we had one fresh-food meal a day, but we were on dry stores for a couple of weeks at a time. Powdered milk is powdered milk. The cooks made pork luncheon meat taste better by frying it in batter. They improved Vienna sausages by baking them in blankets of biscuit dough. But chili is chili, and no cook has ever been able to make the Army's meat and vegetable hash taste like anything better than silage. Fresh game furnished an occasional pleasant change, except for platoons of "A and "B", which temporarily had to hunt to live.

The company PX man set up shop in a separate tent, in which he slept alone to guard his wares. He had to keep simple books and received $25 a month above his pay. He supplied toilet articles and writing materials. He seldom had enough candy and never had enough beer. These he rationed out equally.

During several months we had almost no nights. In June we could sit outside our tents at midnight and read comfortably (as far as the light was concerned; the only time we were comfortable in June was when we passed out). There were two hours of darkness, from 12:30 to about 2:30, but even then only half the sky was really black.

What is otherwise a delightful season in northern Canada, is made almost unbearable by mosquitoes. These voracious creatures, after remaining frozen in dry logs all winter, come out fighting when the weather warms. Thousands of small pools left by the thaw make ideal breeding places. The pests are so numerous that they fly in your mouth when you're talking and stick to your food when you're eating. You swear and swat. They keep coming. When you're on your cot under a mosquito bar, they explore for hours until they find that one small opening you left when you tucked the net under you bedding.

Yukon mosquitoes are storm troopers. Lt. Solterbeck was inspecting a "C" company rifle at the Skyline Drive Camp and jumped about a foot when he saw something coming at him through the barrel.

Repellents were furnished and gave some relief, but had to be re-applied every half-hour. And they were toxic to some of our men, who broke out with hives big as dollars. After the devils attacked us day and night for two solid months, some of us experienced moments of mild hysteria marked by the impulse to lie on the cot and cry. The writer questioned other men who reluctantly admitted that they too had felt like weeping.

Isolation demanded a mental as well as a physical adjustment. Unable to buy entertainment at the box office, we learned how to entertain each other. One company might have a hillbilly singer and guitarist, another a concertina player. We began to understand why the Sourdoughs spoke of their country as inside, the rest of the world, the outside. Being on the inside demanded self-reliance and resulted in the sharpening of our native wit. Ribbing and the creation of nicknames developed into a steady game; "Onionhead," "Halftrack," "Scrapiron," "Beachball," every unit had its clown, its "character," those seldom-promoted, uninhibited, unsung heroes of morale.

What we were beginning to think about is shown by a cryptic entry in the "B" journal: "4 July '42. Big topic of discussion among the men is finishing the road and going home on furlough."

Another thing the men talked about was the regiment's inadequate combat training. On 3 and 4 June the Japs attacked Dutch Harbor, retiring to and occupying Kiska in the Aleutians. We did not know then whether the Japs had the strength to take the Alaska mainland, whether they might not come down the Yukon valleys some day and meet us in the forests. We were combat equipped. We had plenty of .30 and .50 caliber machine guns, halftracks and 37-mm AT guns, but our first air-cooled .50 cal MG's were issued at Whitehorse. We had never fired them. We did not know

enough about land mines. The men said we were not ready.

A few men understood the nature of our mission before we left Vancouver, but the full import of the job was not realized by most of us until it was well under way, until we read it in the magazines. Then we laughed. A man swinging a pick all day has a hard time regarding himself a hero. But we derived satisfaction from pioneering, from feeling the road grow in our hands, with the bite of our axes and massive crush of our dozer blades. Finally, we knew that we were fighting time and the winter deadline. We had the sense of victory. Our own personal victory.

For recreation we had the Band, a very few books, hunting and fishing and a rare visit to a small trading post which offered a few food items. leather articles made by Indians, and no excitement. We were inaccessible to camp shows. Radio reception was poor. Special Service did not come into being until November. A single movie was shown in the ten-month period, in December, Bing Crosby in "Birth of the Blues," and a lot of ice-bound men did not see it.

The Band was our only source of prepared entertainment. It played whole; its band within a band, The Teacoop Five, played specialty numbers; its soloists did their stuff and a few comedy skits were worked up. Being the only entertainment was a handicap, for when the boys saw the Band coming, they were reminded of the forms of fun they didn't have. Yet there was something stirring about those concerts in the lonely valleys; they somehow emphasized our isolation and drew us together in spirit as in fact. And while the music touched off our homesickness, it helped us forget it too.

Mail call was the best phrase we ever heard and reading mail our greatest diversion. At the beginning we endured postal blackouts lasting two weeks. Papers and periodicals were shipped by boat and we read the details of world events two months after they'd happened. Deliveries improved until letters reached us every three or four days.

We submitted to the irony of a censorship straight jacket that forbade our writing about matters which were being openly described in magazine articles.

We learned that foreign service froze ratings, that someone had to transfer or die before another soldier could better himself. We hoped for a cadre to open some ratings, but the cadre didn't happen.

We griped, and managed to have a lot of fun.

By August, mosquitoes were gone and no-see-ums, a gnat whose flying speed makes him invisible, began to raise lumps on us, but this was not so bad.

Autumn lasted from mid-August through September, a time of wind, scattered clouds and light rains, when the Yukon flew its warning signals. The slopes were a pastel metamorphosis of rose, lavender and shade of mustard. The nights lengthened; again we watched the Northern Lights. The air chilled.

The only heavy snow of the winter fell in early October and not a flake had a chance to melt until the following year. Temperatures decreased steadily to about zero, giving us a month of brisk, comfortable working weather.

The nose dive continued through November, ranging from zero to minus forty. Frost thickened on the inner walls of tents, white fingers crept up toward the hoods. Fires that turned the Sibleys orange failed to defrost these iceboxes. A few feet from the stove, canteens froze solid. When we hung clothes on the line, the side toward the fire steamed while the side away froze board stiff. Double down sleeping bags, with blankets added, were none too warm. We slept in fleece-lined helmets and woke to find a pool of frost where our breath had frozen on the bedding.

Gasoline lanterns furnished our only interior light. The price of a lantern rose to $25.

The air was luminous with tiny, gleaming crystals, seemingly in suspension, supporting delicate arctic frostbows.

The air was dry and still. We learned that a few clothes worn loosely were warmer than many layers pressing the skin. At twenty below, if we kept moving, we could work comfortably in arctic jacket, turtle-neck sweaters and fatigue trousers worn over long john woolen underwear. Parts of head and feet were most apt to freeze—were protected by a fleece-lined helmet, knitted woolen gloves and shoepacs worn with one light and one heavy pair of woolen socks and insoles. Gloves hampered the freedom of our hands and we worked as long as we could barehanded, thawing our fingers at open fires. Mechanics had the roughest time, forced to work barehanded continually. Our feet were increasingly in danger of freezing as socks and insoles absorbed perspiration. Drying socks and insoles was a nightly ritual. Some men found cloth-topped overshoes warmer than shoepacs, but the truth was that in respect to footgear only, the Army failed to supply us properly. We should have had mukluks.

We did a lot of work at twenty below, half as much at forty.

At these temperatures men were more effective than machines. We had to keep equipment running day and night if we wanted it to run at all. Before learning this, we spent three days trying to get a truck engine started. Trucks stopped dead on lonely stretches of road, water frozen in the gas lines.

By now the Yukon was a vast white wilderness, thinly, yet completely covered by less than a foot of snow. Beautiful and dangerous.

The swift arctic rivers froze from the bottom up. Pockets of still water at the bottom solidified, built up, but the wild rivers, the Duke, Donjek and White, stubbornly resisted this glaciation. The smaller of their braided channels froze. Finally the deeper channels surrendered, then new water appeared running above the ice. These fighting rivers, vast washboards of ice, on which some water always flowed, defied imprisonment.

The weather lowered the boom in December. Fifty, fifty-five, sixty, finally seventy below. Almost half the regiment was still in tents, where Sibleys now were useless. Each tent improvised a heater from a fifty-five gallon steel gas drum, into which three-foot logs were poured. You could not stand the heat two feet from one of these stoves, yet frost crept up the inner surface of your canvas.

Along Kluane Lake, yellow (glaciers) grew, spread and crept across the road. Geologists may have a better name for these tumors of ice that owe their life to springs of hot water. Near Destruction Bay one sulfurous iceberg developed until it was several miles long, its width blocking half a mile of highway. Early attempts to dynamite an opening failed. It grew to ten feet in thickness and had to be detoured. Trucks were very nearly immobilized. A few faithful D-8 dozers crawled to the northernmost camps where rations were badly needed. Trees froze to their hearts. The Yukon thus won the final round, but wheeled vehicles were able to travel from the states to Alaska for the first time in history. We had won all the earlier rounds and the fight was ours.

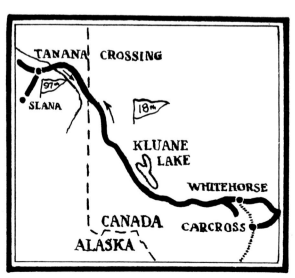

James Alexander O'Connor
(1885-1952)

James Alexander O'Connor was born on July 19, 1885, in West Bay City on Saginaw Bay in Michigan's lower peninsula. He was the son of Charles O'Connor, from County Kerry, Ireland, and Mary Ellen Bissanet Van Paris O'Connor.

His first six years of elementary schooling were in Seney, and he attended three years of high school in West Bay City. He obtained some advanced education at Notre Dame, South Bend, Indiana in 1902-1903.

When in his mid-teens, O'Connor learned of the opportunity of entering the U.S. Military Academy, the idea appealed to him very much. He could satisfy patriotic and career ideals as well as save his parents extra expense. At that time a cadet need pay no tuition, rather he received a small monthly for uniforms and incidentals. He decided to enter this institution, and dropped out of Notre Dame to prepare for the entrance examinations for West Point by home study. Academically he was well-qualified, though his height was a possible handicap, being slightly under the five foot four inch minimum requirement. To overcome this deficiency, he became extremely active in gymnastics and managed to increase his height by one inch in order to qualify.

He entered West Point in June 1903. At the Academy his grade records show mostly high 90's in a wide range of subjects: Algebra, English, Engineering, Literature, Botany, Physics, Bookkeeping and French. He excelled in Geometry, English History and Latin. Without a doubt, James Alexander O'Connor was a scholar rather than a student throughout his life, as he never ceased seeking greater knowledge.

James, also known as Patsy, was graduated from West Point in June 1907, fourth highest in his West Point class of 111 cadets. This earned him the privilege of selecting the Engineer Corps as his branch of the Service, if he so desired.

As a new 2nd Lieutenant, upon graduation, Patsy was sent to Cuba for the 1907 Cuban Pacification duty.

His next duty station was Oahu, Hawaii, in 1909. It was in Hawaii, about 1910, that Patsy met the girl he was to marry. Marjorie Belle Allan was spending a year in Honolulu, accompanying her aunt and uncle, Dr. Ernest K. Johnstone, an Army medical doctor. Lieutenant O'Connor was on engineer duty helping map the island of Oahu.

In 1911 Patsy became a 1st Lieutenant, and had a short stay in Fort Leavenworth early in 1912. In September 1912, he and Marjorie married at her family home in Redlands, California.

As a newly married couple, Patsy and Marjorie went to Washington, D.C., where Patsy's duties included building the foundation of the Lincoln Memorial.

In 1916 Patsy was on duty in El Paso, Texas, and Louisiana with the Punitive Expedition, training Engineer troops. There he became a Major. In 1918 Major O'Connor went to France with the American Expeditionary Forces with the 303rd Engineers in the Rainbow Division (78th). There on June 19, 1918, O'Connor was given a temporary wartime promotion to full Colonel with duty on the front near Verdun and the Meuse River.

He came back to the United States in 1919 to be an instructor at the Engineer School at Camp Humphries, Virginia (now renamed Fort Belvoir).

In 1920 he was on River and Harbor duty on the Mississippi River at Vicksburg, Mississippi, tending to surveyance of the dikes and levee construction. A paddle-wheeler boat belonged to that Engineer office, and was used for inspections of the river projects.

In 1923 Patsy was a student at the Staff and Command School at Fort Leavenworth, Kansas, and later that same year went to Washington, D.C., as District Engineer.

In 1926 Patsy attended the Army War College in Washington, D.C., and in 1927 he returned to Fort Leavenworth, Kansas, as instructor, reaching the rank of permanent Lt. Colonel in 1930 while at the Command and Staff School there. After a serious bout with herpes zoster of the head, he recuperated, and then asked for overseas duty and was sent to Manila, in the Philippine Islands, as Department Engineer, 1931-1934. Here he was in charge of the Engineer Depot with offices in Fort Santiago in the old Walled City.

His next duty station was near the east coast. He arrived in Buffalo, New York, for a three year tour in 1933. While there in Buffalo as District Engineer, he received his permanent rank of full Colonel in 1935. His River and Harbor territory extended from Detroit, Michigan, at the west end of Lake Erie, along the Great Lakes Erie and Ontario, and on down the St. Lawrence River, an area already being studied for the St. Lawrence Waterway project of the following years.

In 1937, Colonel O'Connor was sent to troop duty at Fort Belvoir, Virginia, to command the Fifth Engineer Regiment. O'Connor was Commandant of the Engineer School at Fort Belvoir from 1939 to 1940, then he headed west to be Corps Area Engineer in San Francisco, California. In 1940 he was a member of General Stillwell's staff, and then Army Engineer with General DeWitt in 1941. In 1942, not long after war broke out, O'Connor was put in charge of the southern part of the Alaskan Military Highway construction. Without a doubt this was O'Connor's most demanding and difficult assignment, a race against time.

The thousands of laborers and many Engineer troops under the leadership of General Hoge (West Point, class of 1916), in the north, and O'Connor (West Point, class of 1907) in the south, suffered many trials and tribulations on this 1,671-mile-long road job.

It was while O'Connor was engaged in this most difficult assignment that he received, on Sept. 28, 1942, his commission and his Star as a Brigadier General. As General, O'Connor was then put in charge of the whole Highway, becoming Commander of the Northwest Service Command.

Patsy's next military assignment was in 1944 as Chief Engineer of the China-India-Burma Command with headquarters at New Delhi, India.

In 1945, O'Connor was on duty near Boston, Massachusetts, as Division Engineer. This was his last assignment before retiring in 1946 at the age of 61 due to heart trouble.

After retirement in 1946, he spent the last years of his life in the Los Angeles area with his wife, Marjorie, enjoying gentle games of golf and informal family gatherings. He died suddenly from a heart attack at their home at the age of 66 on March 23, 1952. His wife, Marjorie Allan O'Connor outlived him by almost 25 years, dying at the age of 87 on Dec. 1, 1976. He had four children, three who survived him.

Gen. James Alexander O'Connor, 1942-44. MRS. JOSEPH KILLIAN

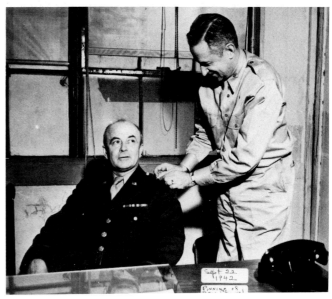

General O'Connor getting his star as a brigadier general, Sept. 22, 1942. MRS. JOSEPH KILLIAN

Bulldozers of varying sizes were the main construction equipment for punching through the initial tote road in 1942. They cleared the right-of-way and roughed out the roadway.
LC-USW33-945-ZC, USW-33-937ZC
& USA SC 141236

This stretch of the tote road, located northwest of Whitehorse, was named "The Grand Canyon of the Alaska Highway." It was named because it was a ditch formed by the thawing of the frozen silt and the gradual draining away of the frozen muck. The passage of equipment only aggravated the almost impossible situation. Places like this could close the road for weeks at a time. NA 30-N-43-3994

This 40-mile section of highway from Pickhandle Lake to Beaver Creek, Yukon, was the great bottleneck on the road. It was impassable until the late summer of 1943 and not completely opened until October 1943. It was pioneered and traveled in the winter of 1942. By spring the roadway had disappeared by the thawing action. Convoys had to be pulled through this section and then followed the ditches to more solid ground. NA 30-N-44-865

Typical conditions along the tote road. Bulldozers were constantly used to push or pull the trucks through washed out or thawed out sections. YA 77/10 U.S. ARMY PHOTO

A typical description of Heavy Equipment operations.*

*Excerpted from the 18th Engineers history.

Equipment performed three principal operations: clearing, cutting and filling, grading.

First, dozer operators rode out to clear a corridor through the woods or brush at least 75 feet wide. Surging in short sweeps lateral to the right of way, the big D-8's rammed, roaring as they razed the soil of trees, brush and boulders. To fall a tree, an operator would shift into the lowest of six forward gears, raise his blade high, approach until the blade rested firmly against the trunk, without pressure. Then, with wide-open throttle, with his face turned up to watch the backlash and for falling limbs, the operator let his clutch in. He could not afford to ease off until the tree was completely off balance and on its way down. After the fall the operator disengaged his blade from the root mass, then pushed the fallen tree forward into the woods. One or two of our men were knocked cold by limbs or trunks, but none were seriously hurt. No Yukon tree could resist the D-8, chiefly because of the absence of tap roots. The hardy trees depended

for growth on a shallow layer of soil often frozen iron hard a foot or two below the surface, causing their roots to fan out in a flat platform at right angles to the trunk. We learned that a single 30-inch tree was easier to topple than a clump of slender, tall ones. These would tangle with each other, break and fall out of control, sometimes toward the catskinner.

Operators were guided in clearing by the double row of stakes set by the 29th Engrs., branches or saplings thrust into the ground, so hard to locate in dense woods that operators often had to clamber down and fight through the brush to find them. When we could ignore the stakes of the 29th to effect a short cut we did so, but the topographic outfit's route was generally followed.

After clearing, cuts and fills were bladed to smooth any wrinkles in the right of way. If possible, cut and fill was made in a single operation, driving your blade through a ridge and spreading the spoilage in the gully beyond, reducing one level and raising the other. The slanted angledozer was useful in cutting dugways in the face of hills. Cuts and short fills were

-34-

legitimate bladework and the irregularity of the terrain made a great deal of it necessary. We were handicapped for long gravel hauls until the arrival in June of six Le Tourneau 23-yard carryalls, whose controls would have baffled our operators anyway, had they arrived earlier. Carryalls were allotted one to a company but "C" ran into trouble and used three or four at a time. Six rooters were delivered and little used.

Grading was the final operation, accomplished by Adams graders usually towed by D-8's, cutting out a road with a 20-foot running surface, ditched on both sides, with spoilage from ditches used to grade the crown. The glacial soil was extremely inconsistent, changing abruptly from red or brown loam to pure gravel with many in-between mixtures, erratic combinations encounterable in a single mile of grading. Because of engine noise, co-operation of tractor and grader operators depended on the former's ability to interpret the hand signals of the man on the grader. The writer used to tow an excitable grader man whose hands signals were mixed with wild haymakers at mosquitoes, producing strange results. Co-operation was particularly necessary where loam contained hidden rocks. When the grader blade struck a submerged boulder and the shearpin failed to break, the light Adams machine would swerve and leave the ground, endangering

its operator. Its frame and rods would be distorted causing its controls to bind, making it tough on operators, but too light for the terrain and powerful D-8. By the time six heavy-duty Caterpillar graders were delivered at the Duke, graders had become useless.

D and R-4's were used to make cuts for culverts, minor cuts and fills and for snaking logs. The D-4 with narrow tracks was a good worker on solid footing but almost helpless in mud. We often wished for D-7's, which could have towed graders and released D-8's for heavier work.

Equipment was going day and night. On every shift, grease monkeys came out in their trucks and located each dozer, checked the gear and crank cases, rollers and filters, while the operator lubricated by hand. Operators also paused briefly when coffee and sandwiches were brought out, and the Alcan Highway was practically paved with discarded pork luncheon meat sandwiches, called Spam? in error.

Most companies used three 8-hour shifts, crews swapping shifts at the end of the week, with relief operators to step in on days off. Ha Ha! "C" used four crews working successive shifts over a 32-hour period, with no relief operators and no day off. Each crew had 8 hours on and 24 off, causing shifts to rotate automatically.

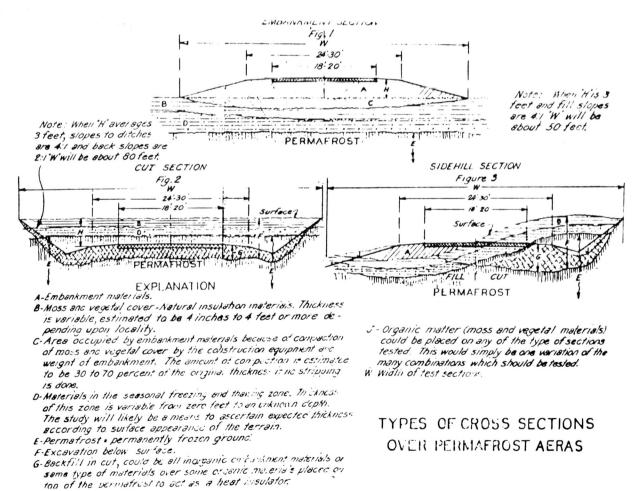

EXPLANATION
A-Embankment materials.
B-Moss and vegetal cover-Natural insulation materials. Thickness is variable, estimated to be 4 inches to 4 feet or more depending upon locality.
C-Area occupied by embankment materials because of compaction of moss and vegetal cover by the construction equipment and weight of embankment. The amount of compaction is estimated to be 30 to 70 percent of the original thickness if no stripping is done.
D-Materials in the seasonal freezing and thawing zone. Thickness of this zone is variable from zero feet to an unknown depth. The study will likely be a means to ascertain expected thickness according to surface appearance of the terrain.
E-Permafrost - permanently frozen ground.
F-Excavation below surface.
G-Backfill in cut, could be all inorganic embankment materials or same type of materials over some organic materials placed on top of the permafrost to act as a heat insulator.

J - Organic matter (moss and vegetal materials) could be placed on any of the type of sections tested. This would simply be one variation of the many combinations which should be tested.
W Width of test sections.

TYPES OF CROSS SECTIONS
OVER PERMAFROST AERAS

On-site repair depots were a necessity to keep the construction equipment running, which took a terrible beating in the wilderness. LC-USW33-935-ZC

Headquarters of the Southern Sector of the highway construction in Fort St. John, B.C. LC-USW33-936-ZC

Hand power was often used even to build rock barriers in streams before bridge construction started. ASL PCA 194-43

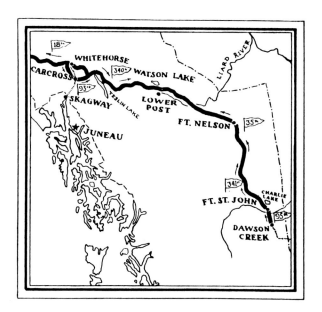

Dog teams were pressed into
service to help stake the right-
of-way in the spring of 1942.
DOROTHY JONES COLLECTION

Army trucks along the
highway drove side-by-side
with an earlier mode of
transportation—the dog sled.
LC-USW33-949-ZC

Wintertime conditions necessitated the thawing of culverts with flame throwers.
NA 30-N-45-28

The use of wooden-stave culverts was widespread along the route. Wooden boxes, steel pipe and even oil drums or whatever was available were also used. NA 30-N-43-3704

The 340th Engineers constructing a log drainage ditch. DOROTHY JONES COLLECTION

Portable sawmills were set up all along the route to provide rough-cut lumber for bridge construction and living quarters. This mill was near Fort Nelson. PABC 37694- (B-5440)

Nothing was too big to haul with enough imagination and resources. River ferries played an important part in the transshipment of material along the route. This 25,000-gallon tank was ferried across the Peace River to be used to fuel highway machines, August 1942. USA SC 141230

A ferry was used at Johnson's Crossing across the Teslin River before the bridge was built. YA #17 PEPPER COLLECTION

A typical "gas station" along the road in March 1942. Jerry cans are being filled from 55 gallon drums to be carried in Army trucks. PAA Bl. 384/7

Rock drills were commonly used along certain stretches of the road, especially at Muncho Lake and Kluane Lake. ASL PCA-193-21

Horses were used along this section of road at Muncho Lake to haul away the rock. NA 30-N-42-1971

Along Muncho Lake.
GORDON PRIEST COLLECTION

Blasting along Mile 106.
GORDON PRIEST COLLECTION

*"Main Street" near
Fort Nelson.*
GORDON PRIEST COLLECTION

A rough road at Mile 162½. GORDON PRIEST COLLECTION

Troops getting a free ride on an improvised raft through the mud. USA SC 139741

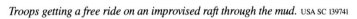

Members of the 95th Engineers lay a corduroy road at Mile 15, in June 1942. USA SC 323248

The tote road at a site between Whitehorse and Kluane Lake, summer of 1942. GA NA-2819-1

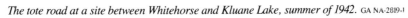

It was found early in the construction process that if the topsoil was stripped off, the underlying permafrost would thaw out and create impassable conditions. Small logs were laid side-by-side to form a corduroy road. USA SC 323259

An unusual straight section of right-of-way in the vicinity of Fort St. John. Stumps piled up by bulldozers are ready for burning. This section cut through dense forests. LC-USZ62-3761Z

Water on the road was encountered on a trip from Whitehorse to Kluane Lake.
H. MALTBIE COLLECTION

Truck convoy. H. MALTBIE COLLECTION

The versatile "Jeep" was in constant use. Even with four wheel drive this vehicle had to chain up to drive over a section of corduroy and pine boughs.
LC-USW33-941-ZC

Typical types of equipment used in construction of the tote road. GHC & BILL HEBERT COLLECTION

The road skirted Kluane Lake, a 50-mile-long lake at the base of the St. Elias Range in the lower Yukon. In this section, many miles of rock had to be blasted away along the lakeshore. PABC 48543 (C-2809)

The highway crossed one and a half miles of silt flats at the mouth of the Slims River at Kluane Lake.
AUTHOR'S COLLECTION

Mile 156. GHC

The pioneer tote road was built without much regard to grades. This would be corrected by the follow-up PRA crews. Four-wheel drive was a must for this section of road.
USA SC 1 43373

GHC

Before the large bridge was built across the Liard River a cable set-up took equipment over. JACK GUNNESS COLLECTION

Suicide Hill was a stretch of road near Pink Mountain, B.C. It was just one of the many obstacles that drivers had to face on the 1,600-mile route to Fairbanks.
AHL & PAA P.6819

A convoy near Steamboat Mountain in northern British Columbia. MILT BRUNSON COLLECTION

A steep grade near Fort Nelson. LC-USW33-933 ZC

Drivers of the first truck from Dawson Creek to Mile 0 at Whitehorse, on Sept. 27, 1942.
NA 30-N-42-5030

Facsimiles of the Burma Shave signs were put up along the road. This one says: "This Road—Will Lead—The Japs—To Hell—So Build—It Quick—And Build—It Well—Buy Burma Shave." NA 30-N-43-3778

Mud was a constant enemy of the road builders and truck drivers. How could one travel faster than five miles per hour? This was the result of a three day rain. NA 30-N-42-5020

First convoy from Whitehorse to Fairbanks, on Nov. 20, 1942. YA 1501 R.A. CARTER COLLECTION

The beautiful Kluane Lake in southern Yukon Territory. YA 1504 R.A. CARTER COLLECTION

Construction along the shoreline of Kluane Lake at Soldiers Summit. BILL HEBERT COLLECTION

Soldiers Summit. H. MALTBIE COLLECTION

Bridge construction over one of the numerous large rivers that the highway had to cross in its 1,500-mile route to Alaska. NA 208-LU-24-G-7

4

BRIDGE CONSTRUCTION

Public Roads Administration Bridges

When the PRA engineers came onto the job in March 1942, they were faced with the best means of crossing numerous rivers ranging up to the size of the Missouri or the upper Missouri. Would the bridges be temporary or permanent?

Although the U.S. War Department in its original directive of Feb. 14 specified permanent structures, in the initial penetration of the country only temporary low-level bridges were to be installed. It later became policy that the temporary wooden bridges should be left intact if they stood up.

Because the rivers in this mountainous country did not behave like ordinary rivers (they were wild, tricky and highly uncertain) the decision to build permanent bridges was made—even though it was estimated the U.S. Army would only require use of the road for four or five years and there was then no commitment from the Canadian government to keep the road open after they were through with it.

The usual placid appearance of the broad, gently flowing Peace, Tanana and Liard rivers belied their ability to rise with startling rapidity to full flood or to carry block-busting ice floes that smashed everything in their path.

Engineers who happened to see for the first time glacial streams like the Duke, Donjek, Robertson, White and Johnson as only trickling currents meandering through mile-wide debris-strewn valleys could scarcely believe these rivers could gush into bank-full torrents within a few hours, rise and fall with the sun as glaciers melted and congealed in varying temperatures of the high mountain ranges, or could pile valley-wide layers of ice up to 30 feet deep.

Other streams of mountain origin like the Muskwa, Sikanni, Chief, Racing River, Toad, McDonald, Trout, Hyland, Coal, Takhini, Yerick, Tok and others are innocent enough at times but could lash out with flood-swollen tongues with devastating suddenness.

All these rivers were as untamed as the country itself. They treated man-made structures with contempt. It took something more than temporary bridges to stand against their fury.

There was no question the major bridges would be permanent ones. The only other question was economy and speed. The engineers looked around for materials immediately available.

A survey by the U.S. Army Corps of Engineers determined structural timber was in short supply due to wartime priorities and unprecedented rains having bogged down lumbering operations. Steel was more readily available. Upon contacting five leading bridge fabricators, it was found substantial inventories of steel were on hand and there was shop space for fabrication. Further studies showed there was little difference in cost between wood and steel. It would be easier to transport steel to the sites.

The initial bridges over the smaller streams were built of native materials that could be found close to the site. Later more permanent structures were built to withstand the spring run-off and heavy truck traffic. JACK GUNNESS COLLECTION

The deciding factor was the bridges had to be high enough and strong enough to allow flash floods and ice to pass underneath.

Having settled the question of type and materials, the next one was speed. This was accomplished by having standard designs prefabricated and having them made up while at the same time having the approaches built all along the highway to accommodate the number of prefabricated spans necessary.

With the standardization of designs, the letting of contracts, manufacture and rolling of steel and fabrication could proceed as soon as the designs were finalized. By the time it

was necessary for details to be filled in for individual bridges, fabrication was well on the way and the field information sent in from Fort St. John and Edmonton to complete the package. Thus there was a great saving of time when time was an important factor.

To further speed up the mass-production technique, the American Bridge Company was awarded a contract for preparation of material lists and shop details for all standard spans for distribution to eight United States and Canadian fabricators. These were prepared in consultation with design engineers in the field.

Building one of numerous small bridges over a creek. Note the mosquito nets, a necessity in the summer months. YA HAYS COLLECTION #17

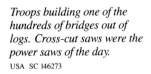

Troops building one of the hundreds of bridges out of logs. Cross-cut saws were the power saws of the day. USA SC 146273

Temporary bridge over the Slims River at Kluane Lake, 1942. LC-USA-33-946-ZC

Driving pilings across the Slims River at Kluane Lake, 1942. H. MALTBIE COLLECTION

An elaborate log bridge. USA, SC 141225

The first bridge constructed across a stream was usually built with pontoons. The permanent log structure was constructed as soon as possible to facilitate two-way traffic and to have a strong structure to withstand the spring run-off. Pontoon bridges could be quickly dismantled and moved to another location. USA SC 141223

Men of the 340th Engineers constructing a log bridge. DOROTHY JONES

Ross River Bridge in the Yukon.
MILT BRUNSON COLLECTION

The first Muskwa River Bridge just south of Fort Nelson. B.C.
GHC

Building the first bridge across the Liard River northwest of Muncho Lake was a major challenge. GHC

*East abutments of the White
River Bridge.*
BILL HEBERT COLLECTION

*The White River Bridge close to completion in 1943. The river crosses the highway at MP/135 (KM 182.7) and was named
by Hudson's Bay Co. explorer Robert Campbell for its white color, caused by the volcanic ash content of the water.* PABC 48550
(C-2816)

A temporary pioneer bridge and a new bridge crossing the Rancheria River, 200 miles southeast of Whitehorse.
AUTHOR'S COLLECTION

Dezadeash River Bridge west of Whitehorse BILL HEBERT COLLECTION

Driving bridge pilings in the Kluane Lake area.
BILL HEBERT COLLECTION

Aishihik River Bridge near Haines Junction.
BILL HEBERT COLLECTION

Constructing a PRA bridge over a major river.
JACK GUNNESS COLLECTION

Temporary bridge across Wolf Creek, B.C. The truck pulling a sled belonged to Jewel Transport of Calgary, Alberta.
GA KATHERINE HOBBERFIELD COLLECTION

Pouring footings on a bridge over the Robertson River. Footings were an average 16 feet below the river channel, seated in dense gravel.

NA 30-N-44-1094

AUTHOR'S COLLECTION

Bridge across the Lewes River just on the outskirts of Whitehorse. A construction camp was located at this site.
NA 30-N-42-5325

GHC

Al Schimberg, PRA bridge engineer at the Contact Creek bridge on Oct. 27, 1943. On Sept. 25, 1942, construction crews working west from Fort Nelson met crews working east from Whitehorse at Mile 567.9. Crews from north and south met at Beaver Creek, Yukon, at Mile 1,168.5 in October 1942, thus opening the entire route to traffic for a few months.
NA 30-N-43-3161

The Kiskatinow River Bridge at MP 20.9 (KM 33.6) between Dawson Creek and Fort St. John is one of the few 1943 bridges still in good condition. The highway bypassed this bridge but the old road is still used for access to the Kiskatinow Provincial Park. GHC

The first bridge across the Sikanni Chief River was a temporary structure built on pontoon barges (left). Then a more permanent structure was built (right), that served for the construction of the permanent bridge. ASL, ALASKA HIGHWAY COLLECTION, PCA 193-47

USA SC 323029

Today, the bridge is still standing and in good condition, however, the realigned highway has long bypassed this section of original construction. AUTHOR'S COLLECTION

The permanent bridge across the Sikanni Chief River, the first completed under the 1943 reconstruction program, was dedicated in the summer of 1943. SC 323029 & SC 322949

Peace River Bridge

The Peace River Bridge at Taylor Flats a few miles south of Fort St. John was the major bridge construction on the highway. The river was so large that it could not be justified to build a bridge to cross it for the low population density in the area. By necessity ferries were used for years on many of the large rivers along the highway route.

However, with construction of the highway proceeding at a rapid pace, it was deemed necessary to build a permanent bridge across the Peace River to carry the anticipated heavy traffic. A ferry just would not be adequate once the highway was opened.

The Public Road Administration (PRA) would build a 2,200-foot suspension bridge at an approximate cost of $3.5 million. The famous bridge firm of John A. Roebling's Sons Co. of Trenton, N.J., was contracted. Roebling was building a suspension bridge in Oakland, Calif., but because of wartime priorities the PRA was able to reroute the steel for the Peace River Bridge.

Dufferin Paving Company of Toronto was given the contract for building the approaches, abutments and piers. One owner of the company, James Franceschini, was ironically, held in a Canadian internment camp for enemy aliens of Italian descent. He was eventually released.

Two piers were built and spaced in the river for a 950-foot center span, with two side spans of 485 feet each. They were 38×80 feet at water level and sunk through 12 to 20 feet of water and 27 feet of gravel to bed rock.

Each pier supported a 195-foot steel tower and the cables were strung across the towers on which a concrete deck was hung. The cables were tied to a 25,000-ton concrete anchor at each end. There were 24 cables on each side, 2⅛-inch in diameter, weighing a total of 13 tons.

The anchors were located at the outer ends of the approach spans and served as the abutments.

The piers were constructed in the winter with temperatures dropping to 50 degrees below zero. In January, the ice was three feet thick and a 68-foot crane was set up on it to erect the steel towers.

To this day it is not certain just how thoroughly the PRA conducted soil tests. The piers probably were not set on bedrock, but a hardpan layer, especially the north pier.

The bridge approaches were typical of rivers in the Canadian North: a high bank on the north, a low bank on the south. A hill fill was necessary on the south approach, a deep cut on the north.

Due to the high priority of the highway, the bridge was built in less than a year, an amazing feat considering the supply limitations, distance from resources, and adverse weather conditions. Between March 25 and April 10, 1943, both towers were erected. On April 11, the ice broke on the river taking out the most recent temporary bridge built by the army. The river fought the bridge construction and ferry operation at every turn. Because of numerous floods it was impossible to use falsework in the channel so a suspension-type bridge was selected. The scouring effect of the water undermined the piers and the high water played havoc with many different types of ferries that were so important to the flow of supplies and men across the river before the bridge was completed.

On Aug. 31, 1943, the bridge was finally opened for vehicle traffic. The ribbon cutting ceremonies took place with United States and Canadian officials.

But this is not the end of the bridge story.

In early 1948, it was discovered that the north pier was being undermined by the scouring water and repairs were immediately necessary. Even with those repairs, however,

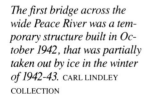

The first bridge across the wide Peace River was a temporary structure built in October 1942, that was partially taken out by ice in the winter of 1942-43. CARL LINDLEY COLLECTION

the heavy truck traffic crossing the bridge to the new petroleum refinery in Taylor and hauling supplies to new enterprises up the highway continued to deteriorate the bridge.

A water line which was strung underneath the structure ruptured in 1957 sending high pressure water into the river. This scoured out gravel once again from beneath the north abutment.

On Oct. 16, 1957, the abutment pulled away from the bank and dropped the entire span into the river below. Because of the importance of the bridge, the government of British Columbia rushed another more substantial structure to completion in January 1960.

Ice breaking up on the Peace River, near the newly constructed piers, April 28, 1943. GHC

Engineers carry a steel trestle piece for the Peace River Bridge onto the north bank of the river, May 3, 1942. ASL U.S. ARMY SIGNAL CORPS COLLECTION, PCA 175-130

Construction of the Peace River Bridge from the north bank in April 1943, was the biggest bridge project on the highway. The Peace River is one of the great rivers of the North and traffic of the early days fur trade was moved on it by canoe.
NA 30N-43-1758

The Peace River Bridge was completed in August 1943. It was the longest bridge on the highway at 2,130 feet costing $4 million dollars. PAA
B1.745/2

On Oct. 16, 1957, the Peace River Bridge collapsed from the tremendous pressure of the river. The present structure was completed in January 1960. SPRHS

Another victim of bad road conditions. USA SC 139766

340th Engineers. DOROTHY JONES COLLECTION

H. MALTBIE COLLECTION

Truck stuck in mud, Dawson Creek, B.C., July 1943. GA J.E. PALMER COLLECTION

SPRHS

YA HAYS COLLECTION

Spring floods. JACK GUNNESS COLLECTION

AUTHOR'S COLLECTION

340th Engineers. DOROTHY JONES COLLECTION

Snow-covered trucks at a camp eight miles north of Fort Nelson.
JACK GUNNESS COLLECTION

GORDON PRIEST COLLECTION

-80-

*Submerged truck 180 miles
north of Fort Nelson.*
GA NA-1796-24

97th Engineers prepare to pull a D-8 caterpillar out of the mud at Slana, Alaska, July 1942. USA SC 322914

SPRHS

340th Engineers. DOROTHY JONES COLLECTION

6

Signs Of The Times

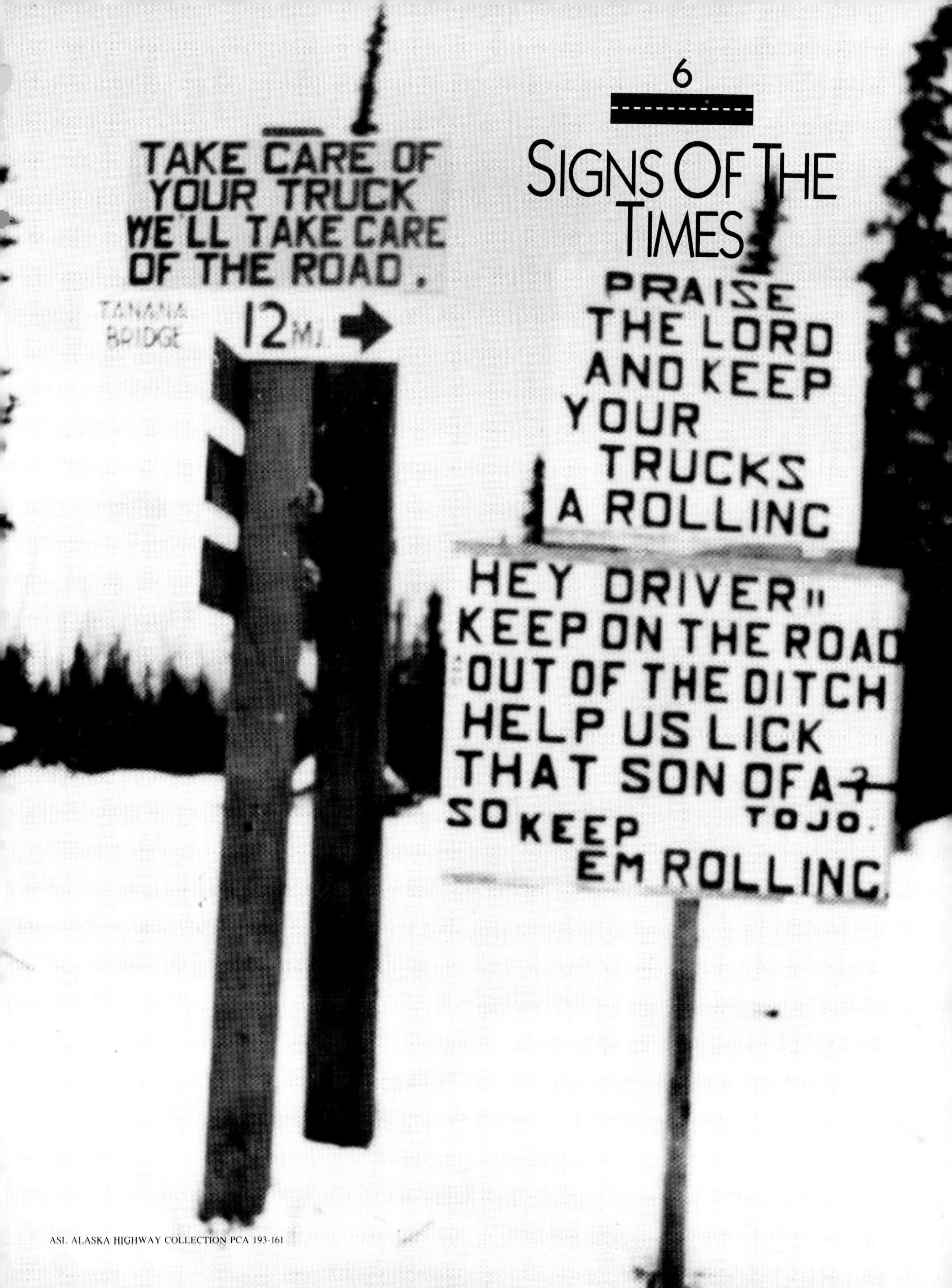
TAKE CARE OF YOUR TRUCK WE'LL TAKE CARE OF THE ROAD.
TANANA BRIDGE
12 MI.
PRAISE THE LORD AND KEEP YOUR TRUCKS A ROLLINC
HEY DRIVER!! KEEP ON THE ROAD OUT OF THE DITCH HELP US LICK THAT SON OF A ? TOJO. SO KEEP EM ROLLINC.

ASL ALASKA HIGHWAY COLLECTION PCA 193-161

Aishihik River camp. BILL HEBERT COLLECTION

NA 208-LU-24-G-4

Carl Lindley at Liard River. CARL LINDLEY COLLECTION

Recollections of Carl Lindley
the originator of the Watson Lake signposts

"I received an injury near the border of British Columbia and Yukon, north of Lower Post. My foot was mashed while building a loading platform to fill dump trucks. I was taken to the company aide station at Watson Lake and spent three weeks there.

"Unable to do much work, the C.O. asked me if I could repair or repaint a sign that was practically destroyed by bulldozers. From the nature of the sign I was encouraged to add my own version and I painted the name of my hometown, Danville, Illinois, on it and put it up along the road."

Lindley's idea caught on as other soldiers nailed up their hometown names and after the war, tourists continued the tradition posting their hometown signs. The area now has more than 14,000 signs and is a major tourist attraction along the Alaska Highway and the site for the major interpretive center along the highway.

Lindley recovered from his injury and returned to his company at the Upper Liard Camp. He continued to make signs and mark trucks until his unit, Company D, 341st Engineers, was transferred back to the States and then to England in November 1943. The company participated in the European Theater of Operations in 1944-45.

After the war, Lindley returned to his hometown and spent 33 years in the printing business. He is now retired.

Sign near Watson Lake, Yukon, July 1943.
YA FINNIE COLLECTION

7

TRANSPORTATION SYSTEMS

Cpl. Albin Sandstrom of Superior, Wisconsin, formerly with the Great Northern Railroad, and Cpl. Michael G. Miatovick of Tracy, Colorado, formerly with the Southern Pacific, both machinists, are shown here repairing the front end of an engine. December 1942. USA

Dog teams were used by the Army in Canada and Alaska where the country was impass-able to other forms of transportation.
USA SC 176081

The airplane played a vital role in the building of the Alaska Highway. Supplies and personnel could be ferried back and forth quickly along the route. The numerous lakes and rivers made float planes highly useful. YA. MacBRIDE MUSEUM COLLECTION 3881 & NA 30-N-44864

A PRA Bellanca and Army Norseman seaplanes on Charlie Lake, just north of Fort St. John, B.C. GA

Bush pilots were the backbone of the aerial force used on both the highway and pipeline projects.
NAC FINNIE COLLECTION PA 175955

A Canadian Airlines plane delivers mail to Dawson Creek.
SPRHS

Sometimes planes did not make a proper landing, as this photo indicates, at the end of the Whitehorse runway.
H. MALIBIE COLLECTION

STEAMBOATS

Like the other transportation systems in Alaska and the Yukon – trains, airplanes, and vehicles – the remaining boats on the Yukon River were called on to contribute to the war effort. But like the other conveyances, the boats were overworked and under-maintained. By 1942, when the huge war-related construction projects were just beginning, the steamboat era was coming to an end. Airplanes and trucks were making inroads into the freight and passenger hauling business on the river.

The remaining steamboats on the Yukon were pressed into service for the war effort as much as possible. Several were used extensively to haul men and supplies on the Yukon lakes to points along the Alaska Highway construction route. Some material was hauled by rail to Whitehorse, put on barges and pushed downriver to Dawson and to Tanana, Alaska, where other boats took over and pushed the barges to Fairbanks, the northern terminus of the highway.

The steamboats had served the war effort well but the end of the river boat era was in sight by 1945.

One of the last sternwheelers on the Yukon River, the Klon-dike was pressed into wartime service to haul supplies from Whitehorse to points down-river. The boat, built in 1936, has been completely restored to that era and is on display in Whitehorse. NA 208-LU-4-4-7 & USA SC 427958

Three majestic riverboats in drydock at Whitehorse. The Klondike *and* Keno *are the last two boats left in the Yukon.* YA PEPPER COLLECTION

The Klondike *on the beach at Whitehorse.*
YA PEPPER COLLECTION

Army vehicles are being off-loaded from a barge at the Dawson City, Yukon, waterfront. While Dawson City was far from the actual highway construction it was on the Yukon River, a major conduit into the interior of Alaska. The few remaining riverboats of the British Yukon Navigation Company were pressed into service along with the railroads and airlines. YA C. HAINES COLLECTION

The Klondike *at Eagle, Alaska, 1943. Eagle Mountain is in the background.*
NAC C-4033

Smaller river boats were used on the rivers in northern Alberta, transferring supplies for both the Alaska Highway and CANOL pipeline projects. LC-USW33-931-20

Even small boats were pressed into service to ferry men and supplies across the wide Peace River before a permanent bridge could be built, April 28, 1943. YA

SPRHS

A Canadian Dept. of Transport ferry operating on the Peace River at Taylor Flats, B.C., May 1942. GA

McLary's Trading Post on Teslin Lake, Yukon, one of the major lakes along the highway route. YA

Ferry across the Peace River between Grande Prairie and High Prairie, Alberta, feeder towns for supplies going to Dawson Creek, B.C. USA SC 207152

The Keno *unloading a barge on the Yukon River.* USA SC 150162

The Keno *at Teslin, Yukon, 1942.* YA PEPPER COLLECTION fi5

The Keno *was a shallow draft sternwheeler that was mainly used on the Stewart River hauling ore to the Yukon River for transshipment to larger river boats. Here it has brought a barge to a point along the Yukon River for unloading. The* Keno *is now on display at Dawson City, Yukon.* YA PEPPER COLLECTION

Barges greatly increased the capacity of the sternwheelers to transport supplies and equipment down the Yukon River. The Keno *is shown at top with its barge being towed to shore. The* White Horse *at bottom is pushing a barge loaded with army trucks.* USA SC 148525 & 150164

The Casca *was another pre-war sternwheeler that plied the upper Yukon River. Barges were pushed ahead, laden with construction material. The* Casca *was destroyed by an arson fire in Whitehorse in 1974.* NA 208-LU-24-G-3

Boats docked at Carcross, a major transshipment point for both the highway and oil pipeline projects. The large boat, Tutshi *had been restored and placed on permanent display at Carcross. Unfortunately it was destroyed by fire in 1990.*
YA PEPPER COLLECTION

Loading pipe on a barge on the Yukon River at Whitehorse. The pipe was destined for the CANOL project. YA PRESTON COLLECTION

WHITE PASS & YUKON ROUTE

The United States' entry into World War II and the decision to build the Alaska (Alcan) Highway had a profound effect on the White Pass Route.

The 1,500-mile route provided only three main access points for the thousands of men and tons of material building up in the South.

One was Dawson Creek, British Columbia, at the southern terminus of the road. Dawson Creek was the end of the Northern Alberta Railroad and was connected by road to Edmonton, Alberta, and points south. The second was Fairbanks, the northern terminus of the highway. Fairbanks was connected to Anchorage and the sea by the Alaska Railroad and the Richardson Highway.

The third was Whitehorse, the terminus of the most important link to the interior of the Yukon: the White Pass Route from Skagway. Men and materials could be shipped up the inside passage to Skagway, hauled on the railroad to Whitehorse, and then sent north and south along the highway.

In addition to supplying the Alaska Highway project in 1942-43, the railroad carried material for the CANOL construction project, a road and pipeline built by the U.S. Army from Norman Wells, Northwest Territories, to pipe oil to a Whitehorse refinery used by the military.

Construction of the highway began in March 1942, and it was determined at once that help was needed to keep the trains running.

Although the railroad could handle peacetime demand, it was overwhelmed by the quantity of material needed for the two construction projects. The docks at Skagway and the railroad's equipment were both inadequate. Most of the equipment, left over from the Gold Rush days, was practically worn out. Fewer than a dozen engines were in working order, and the roadbed was desperately in need of repair.

So the railroad was leased to the U.S. government for the duration of the war, and the U.S. Army took over its operation, retaining the civilian employees. The 770th Railway Operating Battalion of the Military Railway Service officially assumed control on Oct. 1, 1942, and operated the White Pass Route until the war was over. Most of the men in the battalion were from Southern states, and on their official introduction to the North country they encountered one of the worst winters in its history. Construction was started on many buildings and shops in Skagway and Whitehorse to accommodate the troops and material being assembled for construction of the road.

Rolling stock was built at the repair yards in Skagway, and even one of the old locomotives that had run to the Klondike gold fields was pressed into service.

Engines Nos. 10 and 14 were shipped north in 1942 by the Army. They had been built originally for the East Tennessee and Western North Carolina Railroad. Engines Nos. 20 and 21 came from the Colorado and Southern Railroad, and Engines Nos. 22, 23 and 24 from the Silverton Northern, in 1943. All of these locomotives had been built by Baldwin in the late 1890s and early 1900s.

In 1943, 10 steam engines consigned to Iran were diverted to Skagway, converted from metered gauge to the three-foot gauge and used for the rest of the war. The engines, all 2-8-2s (a wheel alignment designation) built by Baldwin for the U.S. Army, were numbered 190 through 200. All were scrapped or sold after the war except No. 195, which is on display at the Trail of 98 Museum in Skagway.

Seven additional narrow-gauge engines built in 1923 by American Locomotive were purchased from the Denver, Rio Grande and Western Railroad in 1942 and used until 1945.

During the war the railroad accumulated 36 engines and

almost 300 freight cars, some built for service in South America. More than 280,000 tons of material were carried to Whitehorse in 1943 — 45,000 tons in August alone. Thousands of troops and construction workers were also carried in both directions.

At the height of operations in 1943, dozens of trains rolled between Skagway and Whitehorse every day. As the war approached its end, the pressure eased, and none too soon. The railroad was literally worn out.

The 770th Railway Operating Battalion continued to run the railroad until control was returned to the pre-war management on May 1, 1946.

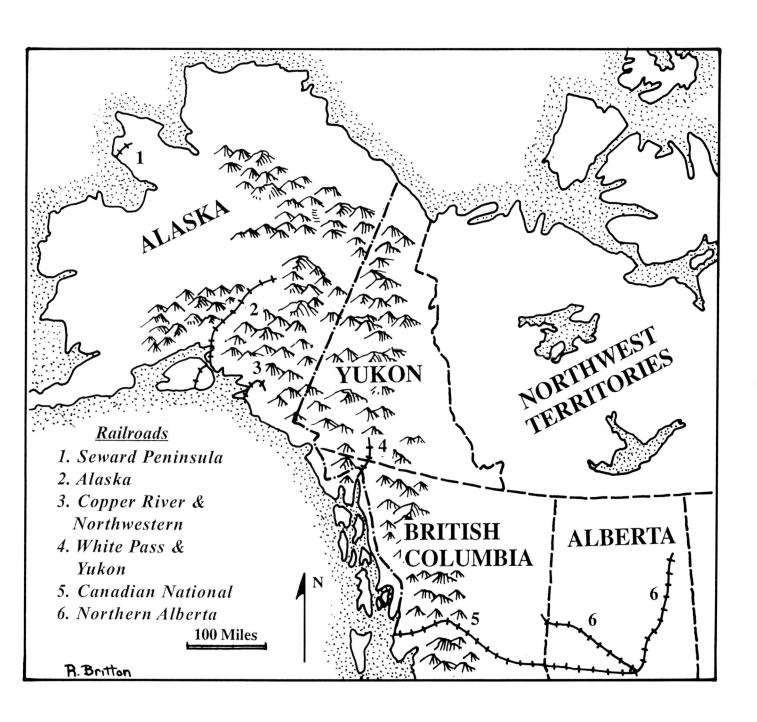

Railroads
1. *Seward Peninsula*
2. *Alaska*
3. *Copper River &*
   Northwestern
4. *White Pass &*
   Yukon
5. *Canadian National*
6. *Northern Alberta*

100 Miles

N

R. Britton

Track of the White Pass & Yukon Route, laid down Broadway Street in Skagway, came to life again during World War II. The tracks were moved to the edge of town after the war. ASL

Troops of the Railway Battalion at the Skagway railyards.
DEDMAN'S PHOTO SHOP

Pulling into town after a run to Whitehorse, December 1942.
USA

Troops of Company B, 770th Railway Operating Battalion, at the Skagway roundhouse, March 1944.
DEDMAN'S PHOTO SHOP

Personnel of the 770th Railway Operating Battalion at Whitehorse.
YA PRESTON COLLECTION #187

Headquarters and Supply Company of the 770th Railway Operating Battalion at Skagway.
YA PRESTON COLLECTION #170

770th Railway Operating
Battalion at the Whitehorse
roundhouse.
YA PRESTON COLLECTION #178

The White Pass & Yukon Route
was a twisting, narrow gauge
railroad built in 1900 to service the Klondike gold fields
500 miles to the north. It was
severely overtaxed during the
war years.
USA SC 163100-B

Railyard at the north end of Skagway in 1944. NA 208-LU-5-Q-1 & 208-LU-4-Z-2

The Wye at Whitehorse.
YA PRESTON COLLECTION #28

*Camp of the 770th Railway
Operating Battalion at the Wye
in Whitehorse.*
YA PRESTON COLLECTION #48

*The only railroad crossing
over the Alaska Highway near
Whitehorse, 1944.* USA SC 323052

Maj. John E. Ausland, the military superintendent of the White Pass, talks with one of his firemen, Pvt. Ross Weye of Havre, Montana, in December 1942. Ausland formerly had been with the Burlington Route. USA SC 163090-B

Train leaving Skagway for Whitehorse, December 1942. USA SC 163120-B

The steel bridge over Deadhorse Canyon was put under armed guard at the beginning of the war. A sabotage attempt on this bridge was foiled by guards; there had been no time for the saboteur to attach the plunger to the wires, even though the explosives had been laid in at the bridge footings. No one was ever caught for the attempt. Related by Col. Corbett Coil, 770th Commander in Skagway. 11TH AIR FORCE

Sgt. William Howard, conductor on the railroad, collects a ticket from Miss Margaret Johnston at Skagway, December 1942. USA SC 163098

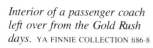

Interior of a passenger coach left over from the Gold Rush days. YA FINNIE COLLECTION fi86-8

Unloading pipe for the CANOL project at Carcross.
YA FINNIE COLLECTION H-158 #80-12

Troops boarding the train at Skagway for Whitehorse. Some of the passenger cars were left over from the Gold Rush days 42 years earlier. USA SC 150182

Loading supplies in Skagway for shipment to Whitehorse and to the Alaska Highway construction project, 1942. LC

Every engine, even some dating back to the gold rush days, was pressed into service to keep the trains rolling night and day.
YA PEPPER COLLECTION #37

Heavy equipment was shipped up the Inside Passage to Skagway and then transported by rail to Whitehorse where it was dispersed up and down the highway right-of-way.
YA PRESTON COLLECTION #153

Sgt. Xaviour A. Athey, an MP, checks credentials of passengers on board a train heading for Whitehorse, December 1942. USA SC 163101

Carcross, Yukon, showing the station and warehouse on the right and the railroad bridge on the left. All of this still exists today. YA FINNIE COLLECTION

The White Pass & Yukon Route station at Whitehorse, built in 1900, was the scene of much activity during the war.
YA FINNIE COLLECTION & PRESTON COLLECTION #3

*Engine No. 10 was severely
damaged in a fire at the
Whitehorse roundhouse.*
YA PRESTON COLLECTION #61

*Mishaps sometimes occurred
even in the best of weather
conditions. Engine No. 71
derailed just past the station at
Whitehorse in 1943.*
YA FINNIE COLLECTION

*Engine No. 195 on display
next to city hall in Skagway. It
was built to meter gauge in
1943 for use in Iran but was
diverted to Skagway, con-
verted to narrow gauge and
used until the end of the war.*
AUTHOR'S COLLECTION

Snow on the track north of White Pass. USA SC323129

An engine plows through a 16-foot snowbank at White Pass. Some of the worst winter weather in years occurred during the winter of 1942-43. USA SC 283623

Bennett Station on Feb. 21, 1943. YA

Everybody had to help dig out the trains. Rotary snowplows were effective most of the time. USA SC323098

Even large snowplows could have trouble cutting through the deep drifts. When wet snow fell and the temperature dropped, the snow froze as hard as concrete. In this view from 1944, soldiers try to repair a damaged snowplow. USA SC 200220

The Whitehorse-Skagway telephone line, amid deep snow, winter of 1944-45. USA SC 247714

The winter of 1944-45. USA SC247709 & 247722

Conditions on the railroad were very harsh during the winter of 1944-45. USA SC 247712

The snow conditions caused many accidents during the expanded use of the railroad from 1942-45. USA SC 247718

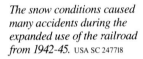

On Lake Bennett, winter of 1944-45. USA SC 247720

Engine No. 195 pulls a train at Bennett Station, 1944. USA SC 323064

Like its railroad, Skagway's main dock (formerly Moore's Wharf) was heavily overworked during the war years. Supplies and personnel for both the Alaska Highway and the CANOL pipeline project were funneled through Skagway on their way to Whitehorse. USA SC 323262

The Skagway dock. USA SC 163102-B, 322938

Aerial view of the Skagway dock and facilities, May 1945. A large portion of the materials for the Alaska Highway and CANOL pipeline projects came through this dock on their way to the Yukon interior. USA SC 323312

Engine No. 81 at the Skagway dock. DEDMAN'S PHOTO SHOP

The Skagway dock. In the background can be seen what is called The Ship's Log, a rock formation on which names of ships that docked there were painted.
USA SC 163094-B

ALASKA RAILROAD

Even before the attack on Pearl Harbor, the Alaska Railroad was intimately involved in building Alaska's defenses. With the establishment of military bases in Anchorage and Fairbanks in 1940 and 1941, the railroad experienced a dramatic increase in its haulage. At the same time, the railroad found it increasingly difficult to obtain labor due to increased military activity in Alaska and the Lower 48.

The increase in traffic and the inconvenience of shuffling staff members from the terminal site to the federal building prompted the railroad to begin construction of a three-story depot and general office building in Anchorage. It was completed in 1942 and is still in use today. To alleviate a bottleneck in traffic on the Kenai Peninsula, the railroad in 1941 also began construction, at a cost of $5.3 million, of that spur to the Passage Canal known as the Whittier Cutoff.

When the United States entered the war, the railroad became even more closely involved with Alaska's defense. Alaska was put under control of the Army, while the railroad was watched by civilian guards placed at strategic points along its route. A bypass was built around the Kenai Peninsula "loop" to speed the flow of goods and as a precaution against enemy air attacks. A blackout rule, put in force throughout the state, made wintertime train operations hazardous.

The war also caused the railroad to undergo a labor shortage as many of its employees joined the military or left for higher-paying jobs. This problem was compounded by a critical shortage of locomotives and freight and passenger cars. Finally, the Alaska Defense Command loaned some soldiers to keep the trains operating and additional rolling stock was brought in, some of it from the defunct Copper River and Northwestern Railroad.

But these measures were not enough. By early spring 1943, it was obvious that something had to be done to keep the railroad operating in a safe and efficient manner. Help was on its way in the form of the 714th Railway Operating Battalion, a part of the U.S. Army Transportation Corps.

Activated at Camp Claiborne, La., in March 1942, the battalion was made up for the most part of experienced railroad men from the Chicago, St. Paul, Minneapolis and Omaha Railroad. It was ordered to travel to Fort Lewis, Wash., to pick up additional track-maintenance personnel, and it headed for Alaska with a total of 23 commissioned officers, two warrant officers, and 1,092 enlisted men.

The battalion landed at Seward on April 3, 1943, and immediately went to work to augment the railroad's slim civilian

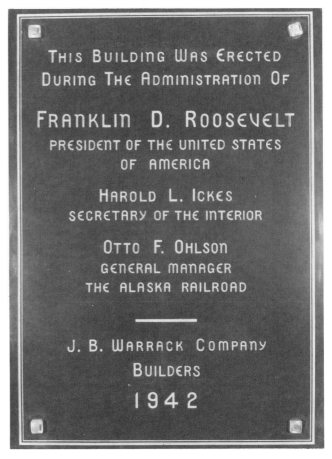

The old and new Alaska Railroad stations at Anchorage, 1942. AMHA

AMHA

-116-

workforce. Maintenance was at a low ebb, and, due to the manpower shortage, there was a tremendous backlog of material piled up at Seward.

The opening of the port of Whittier later in 1943 alleviated some of this backlog, and other aid also came in 1943 with the arrival of six new locomotives, built by Baldwin for use overseas and numbered 551 to 556, similar to the 500-class locomotives already in service on the Alaska Railroad. Still, the men of the 714th had all they could contend with trying to run the railroad in tough winter conditions with barely enough personnel to do the job.

The Army also supplied soldiers for another vital railroad activity. A coal shortage developed in Alaska during the war due to the military's demands for fuel and the lack of miners to supply it. Thus the Army sent soldiers to keep the railroad's Eska coal mine open between 1942 and 1945.

During the war, Army personnel in Alaska sometimes stayed at the McKinley Park Hotel, which had been taken over by the Army as a recreation camp. The railroad operated a Brill car and trailer to the hotel from Anchorage, making a round trip each week.

In the aftermath of the expulsion of the Japanese from Alaska in 1943, the military relaxed a little, and its presence began to diminish in the territory. The War Manpower Commission recruited more civilian workers for the railroad in early 1945, and the 714th was released in May of that year.

With the end of the war, the railroad returned to its prewar schedule. The war had been an exhausting trial for the railroad, and considerable capital was needed to bring it back to safe operating conditions. But, with its return to a civilian role, the railroad knew it had contributed in its own way to the war effort.

The Fairbanks station.
HENRY HUNT

Otto F. Ohlson, general manager of the railroad, poses in front of the Curry Hotel with his Dodge railmobile, 1938. Ohlson guided the railroad through much of its early development, including the World War II years. His tenure ran from 1928 to 1945.
AMHA

An Army MT boat, one of the shallow-draft tugs used in rafting operations on the Tanana River, brought to Nenana by flatcar in 1944. USA SC 207110

The Army's operations spanned more than 400 miles of railroad, and the PX had to be located where the Army was operating. This mobile PX moved up and down the line, dispensing personal items such as toilet articles, cigarettes, candy and magazines. The motor coach and trailer, sometimes called the "galloping goose" or "gray goose," occasionally served as an ambulance.
USA SC 337850, 176686

Troop sleeper cars. AMHA

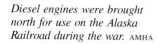

Diesel engines were brought north for use on the Alaska Railroad during the war. AMHA

Dock facilities at Whittier, June 1943. With the completion of the cutoff in late 1942, Whittier provided a much shorter and safer route to Anchorage for the thousands of tons of cargo that were pouring into Alaska during the war. AMHA

General view of Whittier area, looking northeast, June 1943. The railroad yards are on the left and the dock area is in the center background. AMHA

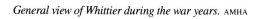

General view of Whittier during the war years. AMHA

View of the upper end of Whittier, showing the U.S. Army barracks, September 1943.
AMHA

The Whittier railroad station, May 1944. USA SC 571430

The Whittier dock in 1943.
AMHA

Holing-through ceremonies on Nov. 20, 1942. Col. Otto F. Ohlson, left, shakes hands with Maj. Gen. S.B. Buckner. AMHA

Before setting off the blast to open the tunnel to Whittier, Maj. Gen. Simon B. Buckner, commander of the Alaska Defense Command, and party gather at the tunnel entrance, Nov. 20, 1942. AMHA

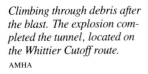

Climbing through debris after the blast. The explosion completed the tunnel, located on the Whittier Cutoff route. AMHA

Camp Americanada at Dawson Creek, B.C. GHC

8

CONSTRUCTION CAMPS

*Tent town at Dawson Creek,
January 1942.* GA A. IKERT
COLLECTION

*Headquarters camp at Fort St.
John, April 21, 1942.* USA SC
322869

*A sawmill was set up in this
early highway camp to supply
building materials and
firewood.* LC USW 33-951-ZC

18th Engineers camp at Whitehorse on May 4, 1942. Men are gathering at front of the tent at the end of street which is the kitchen for the Headquarters and Service Company. YA ROBERT HAYS COLLECTION 5698

A large camp of Army bell tents at Whitehorse. A C-47 is just coming in for a landing at the Whitehorse Airport. YA ROBERT HAYS COLLECTION 5694

P-X tent of an 18th Engineers camp. YA H.E. BARLEY COLLECTION 5516

View of two long rows of bell tents at a camp at Whitehorse, May 21, 1942. The photo was taken immediately prior to the striking of the camp. YA ROBERT HAYS COLLECTION 5697

Photos of A Company 648th Engineers Topographic Battalion. VIA TED MIDUSKI

Construction camp along Summit Lake, the highest point on the road. NA 30-N-44-844

Construction camp at Watson Lake. The use of the portable and fast-erecting Quonset huts was widespread during the construction period. PABC

Camp at Lower Post, B.C. GHC

Elliott Construction camp at Kluane Lake.
BILL HEBERT COLLECTION

Liard River Camp. GHC

Sikanni Chief River Camp, Milepost 163. GHC

A trapper's cabin was used as temporary quarters for nurses while a hospital was being built at Muskwa near Fort Nelson for the U.S. Public Health Service. NA 30-N-43-3493

*The more permanent head-
quarters camp at Fort St.
John. 1943.* GA J.E. PALMER
COLLECTION

*R.M. Smith Construction
Company at Dawson Creek,
July 1943.* GA J.E. PALMER
COLLECTION

*PRA living quarters at Fort St.
John, 1943.* GA J.E. PALMER
COLLECTION

The camp of the Dufferin Construction Company near Taylor, B.C. GHC

BPC Camp at Muncho Lake, B.C. GHC

Camp of the E.W. Elliott Construction Company at Kluane Lake. BILL HEBERT COLLECTION

New tires stacked at Elliott's camp at Kluane Lake. BILL HEBERT COLLECTION

Upper crossing of the Liard River,. Co. D. 341st Engineers camp on right.
CARL LINDLEY COLLECTION

Dust respirators were worn by men working on parts of the highway. After the highway dried out the constant stream of trucks and equipment ground the earth into a fine dust, sometimes up to six inches deep. The dust caused considerable driving hazards with truck convoys.
LC USW 33-952-ZC

A GI going to chow at a camp in Skagway.
YA PRESTON COLLECTION

9

LIFE ALONG THE HIGHWAY

Surveyors, 1942. Mosquito nets were an absolute necessity for outdoor work in the summer months.
BILL HEBERT COLLECTION

NA III-SC-I43332

YA HAYS COLLECTION

NA 208-LU-24-G-6

Rain or snow the men had to be fed, unfortunately sometimes outside. YA HAYS COLLECTION

The Bands

The 35th Regimental Band.
MILT BRUNSON COLLECTION

Concert at the old town of Silver City, Yukon.
YA MACBRIDE MUSEUM COLLECTION

18th Engineers Band playing at the White Pass & Yukon station in Whitehorse.
YA PEPPER COLLECTION

Church services. NA 30-N-42-5108

A civilian work crew camped near the completed Sikanni Chief River Bridge, 1943. GA C. HAGE COLLECTION

Surveyor's tent in the Yukon, 1942. BILL HEBERT COLLECTION

Fresh game was always a welcome relief from ordinary army chow. ASL

"Pets" from the forest often begged for food. SPRHS

"Home Sweet Home," spring 1942. CARL LINDLEY COLLECTION

Home was where you hung your hat. SPRHS

A post office was set up in a bell tent at a camp at Kluane Lake, 1942. H. MALTBIE COLLECTION

Wash Day. MILT BRUNSON & ASL PCA 193-152

Camp scenes. MILT BRUNSON COLLECTION

Christmas party for the 843rd Signal Service Battalion, 1943. NA III-SC-323043

Not only was the mosquito the scourge of the construction men but the black fly also took its toll. The bites caused large swellings and much discomfort. Mosquito nets were a necessity for men working in the outdoors during the height of the season. NA 30-N-43-3776

GORDON PRIEST COLLECTION

Survey Crew. GORDON PRIEST COLLECTION

The bitter cold was very hard on the construction workers, especially the black troops of the South, most of whom had never seen snow. ASL

Liard Hot Springs near Milepost 497 was a natural recreation spot just off the highway. It could warm up a body in a hurry in the dead of winter. USA SC 323237

Guard duty in the camp of the 340th Engineers. DOROTHY JONES COLLECTION

Reveille. MILT BRUNSON COLLECTION

Baby moose being fed at a camp at Muncho Lake.
JACK GUNNESS COLLECTION

Harold Maltbie at the front of his tent at Kluane Lake, fall
1942. HAROLD MALTBIE COLLECTION

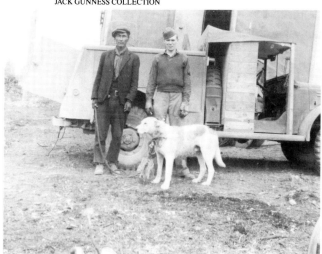

Charlie McDonald, a local Indian trapper and his dog, Dead
Line, with a GI in the vicinity of Muncho Lake.
JACK GUNNESS COLLECTION

Not only did the highway open up the North Country for motorized traffic but it afforded the native people easier access to the outside world. This is Patsy Henderson and his wife, well-known characters from the Klondike Gold Rush, four decades before. NA 30-N-43-1876A

10

COMMUNITIES
ALONG THE ROAD

WELCOME
TO
FORT ST. JOHN

Prince Rupert, B.C., located on the Pacific Coast at the terminus of the Canadian National Railroad, became a major transshipment point for troops and supplies heading north for highway and pipeline construction and for operations in the Aleutian campaign. AUTHOR'S COLLECTION

Ponce Coupe, B.C., a few miles east of Dawson Creek, was a small village that had the only liquor store in the Peace River country. GA NA-1411-3

In the early 1940s, Dawson Creek, B.C., had a population of 500-600 and was the center of the Peace River wheat country and the northern railhead of the Northern Alberta Railroad. In the spring of 1942, Dawson Creek became the jumping off point for construction of the Alaska Highway. By 1943, the population had mushroomed to many thousands. Today, the bustling city is Mile 0 on the Alaska Highway. PAA H. POLLARD COLLECTION

The downtown section of Dawson Creek, January 1944. USA SC 323081

Dawson Creek, at the end of the railroad, was the major jumping off point for the southern section of highway construction. Thousands of troops poured into town in the spring of 1942 and thousands of civilians followed for the reconstruction in 1943. All the facilities in town were severely overtaxed and the U.S. Army upgraded sewer, water and medical systems to meet the needs of troops and local citizens alike. SPRHS

WSON CREEK

On Feb. 13, 1943 the Miller Construction Company warehouse in Dawson Creek caught on fire. Both the U.S. Army and local firemen fought the fire and thought they had brought it under control. Without warning the building suddenly exploded with a force that levelled a complete city block in the downtown center. Five people were killed and more than 150 were injured by flying glass and debris that rained down from the sky. The blast was felt seven miles away in Pouce Coupe. The fire, the origin unknown, seemed fairly routine but no one knew that a truck loaded with five tons of dynamite and several cases of blasting caps had been placed in the building for storage, the night before.
ORVAL COUCH. WHITEHORSE. YUKON

Dawson Creek Catastrophe

SATURDAY' FEBRUARY 13th 1943.

By EUGENE WILKINSON

'Twas a balmy Saturday evening
In the Boom-Town Dawson Creek
A soft chinook was blowing
And the streets were icy slick.

There were farmers with their
    wives and kids
And soldier boys galore
And dozens of lads from construc-
    tion jobs
They filled each lighted store

The springlike air seemed to fill
    each heart
And the world seemed bright and
    warm
As they gaily mingled and milled
    about
Without a thought of harm

And unaware of hovering doom
Each one but little knew
What pain and suffering they
    would see
Before the night was through

Laughter tinkled and voices rang
Like music everywhere
Then each was tense as the mourn-
    ful whine
Of the siren filled the air

A column of smoke rose o'er the
    town
As the angry flames grew white
And it drew each one like a
    magnet
To its circle of glowing light

They stared in fascination
As they filled the narrow street
While the firemen fought courage-
    ously
In the fierce and blistering heat.

Unheeded went the warning cry
"Keep back". There's dynamite".
For we all knew the stuff would
    burn
That is, until that night

Just then the whole town heaved
    and shook
With the terrific deafening Blast
And the country was lit for miles
    around
By the mighty blinding flash

Bodies were flung like stones from
    a sling
Sparks rained all over town
And flaming tires and timbers
Covered people on the ground

In every direction people ran
Shouting and screaming in terror
While others lay kicking and
    squirming
Oh God! What a price for an error.

The eerie flare of the unleashed
    flames
Was all that lit the scene
Of the most stunning fire disaster
This country has ever seen

Hats and caps lay strewn around
And the flesh and tattered clothes
Scattered along that block of hell
Would make your blood run cold.

The bedlam and panic could not be
    described
By any human pen
As the leaping flames lashed out to
    bring
This town to a violent end .

The Frontier Lumber Company
And the Alcan Tire Shop next
The blacksmith shop and Central
    Garage
Were all a total wreck.

As the angry flames with leaps and
    bounds
Took everything in their path
The Dawson Hotel and poolroom
Seemed the object of their wrath.

The Dawson Hotel, well known by
    all,
Was one of the country's first.
Where many a man in history
Had stopped to quench his thirst.

But fickle fate in a vicious mood
Was wont to play no favor.
So she was borne down with the
    rest
In spite of the fight to save her.

The boys then turned to the Co-Op
    store
Not far from the old hotel.
And their valiant tireless battle
Kept her from that brink of hell.

The boys deserve a medal
That were fighting there on top
Though the heat burned through
    to their very bones
They still stayed on and fought.

The credit is due to the army
And their handling of the task.
That Dawson Creek is still a town
Instead of a blackened mass.

There's many a heavy heart tonight
Among the boys in town
For many faces are missing now
That used to be seen around.

With its boarded up doors and
    windows
And deserted looking street
They ought to change its nickname
    now
To Ghost-Town, Dawson Creek.

Fort St. John, B.C., was founded in 1806 as a trading post for the local Sikanni Indians. It was a sleepy village until the Canadian government built an airbase here in 1941. Its population expanded greatly during the construction period and now is a bustling center for commerce and industry in northeastern British Columbia GA and NA 30-N-42-5339

The Hudson's Bay trading post at Fort Nelson, B.C. AUTHOR'S COLLECTION

In early 1942, Fort Nelson, B.C., consisted of a few log cabins, the Hudson's Bay trading post, store, RCMP police detachment and the Yukon Southern Air Transport radio station. It is now one of the major cities along the highway. USA SC 141234

Lower Post, B.C., just a few miles southeast of Watson Lake, Yukon, was an early Hudson's Bay trading post.
ASL & PABC

The trading post at Teslin, Yukon, was an important construction site at the southern end of the territory.
AUTHOR'S COLLECTION

Watson Lake, Yukon, the gateway to the territory at Mile 600 was another important stop on the Northwest Staging Route and an important construction site.
USA SC 322942

Shops, construction equipment and trucks with pipe for the CANOL project at Whitehorse.
UAA W.G. VANDERBURG COLLECTION 86-152-2

Whitehorse Station, 1942. BILL HEBERT COLLECTION

Tents, barracks and warehouses sprang up all over Whitehorse during the construction period.
UAA W.G. VANDERBURG COLLECTION 86-152-1

Main Street in Whitehorse with the railroad station at the end of the street. USA SC 323244 & NA 30-N-44-820

Whitehorse, in southern Yukon, was a small community in 1942. It was the terminus of the White Pass & Yukon Route and the starting point for sternwheelers servicing the communities along the Yukon River. The town was established as the northern headquarters for the Northwest Service Command in the spring of 1942 and its population expanded tenfold. Today, Whitehorse is the capital of the Yukon and the major service and distribution center for the entire territory.
YA KAMLOOPS MUSEUM COLLECTION

The White Pass & Yukon Route Station at the end of Main Street in Whitehorse was a busy place during the construction phase. The building is now used for office space.
YA KAMLOOPS MUSEUM COLLECTION

Whitehorse with the frozen Yukon River in the foreground. Large warehouses lined the river during the war years.
NA 30-N-43-3839

Whitehorse from the bench above town. The Yukon River is in the background and part of the airport in the foreground. Many of the U.S. Army's new buildings can be seen in town. Whitehorse was a major stop on the Northwest Staging Route from the United States to Fairbanks, Alaska. YA FINNIE COLLECTION

The Yukon River was the major transportation artery in the territory prior to construction of the Alaska Highway. In the background are benches above the town, where the airport was located. USA SC 331172

A large construction camp and supply and distribution center was established at McCrae, Mile 910 in 1942. The site, southeast of Whitehorse, is now an industrial area.

USA SC 231263

1940s menu.

The government liquor store in Whitehorse was perhaps the busiest place in town, especially on weekends.

YA U.S. ARMY PHOTO

Whitehorse Grill

★
Sandwich Menu
★

Hot Beef Sandwiches and Coffee 70c

Steak Sandwich . . . . ⌃ ‑ .80c

Oyster Sandwich on Toast 60c

Cheeseburger Sandwich 45c

Tuna Fish Sandwich 35c
(Fine Chopped Celery and Mayonaise)

Chicken Salad Sandwich . . . ⋮ 50c
(Chopped Chicken, Mayonaise and Pickle)

Bacon and Tomato Sandwich . . . . . ; 35c

Sardine Sandwich 25c

Ham and Tomato Sandwich 35c

Cold Pork or Beef Sandwich 25c

Clubhouse Sandwich .75c

Devilled Egg Sandwich 25c

Hot Chicken Sandwich 1.00
(Soup, Pie and Coffee)

Club Sandwich 60c

Grilled Ham and Cheese Sandwich 50c

Champagne was a small native village about 50 miles west of Whitehorse on the right-of-way of the highway. Like many other villages and towns along the route, its character would be changed forever. BILL HEBERT COLLECTION

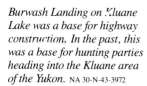

Burwash Landing on Kluane Lake was a base for highway construction. In the past, this was a base for hunting parties heading into the Kluane area of the Yukon. NA 30-N-43-3972

Carcross, between Skagway and Whitehorse, was on the main line of the White Pass and Yukon Route and became a major transshipment point, especially for the CANOL project. The Matthew Watson General Store and Caribou Hotel still exist today. PAC FINNIE COLLECTION

Street scenes in Fairbanks, Alaska, during the war years.
UAA WILLIAM S. CRAIG COLLECTION

Waterfront of Fairbanks in December 1943, at the northern terminus of the highway. Fairbanks was a gold mining town from the early 1900s and became very important in the defense of Alaska during the war. USA SC 323013

Broadway Street in Skagway during the war. YA FINNIE COLLECTION

Skagway, Alaska in 1945. Skagway went from a gold rush boom town in 1898 of 10,000 people to a near ghost town in the early 1940's. It was the southern terminus of the White Pass and Yukon Route and figured prominently in the building of the A laska Highway and CANOL project. In March 1942 it became a boom town once again when the railroad was pressed into wartime service. USA SC 323299

Skagway, 1943. NA 80-CF-78145-1 & DEDMAN'S PHOTO SHOP

11
THE HAINES HIGHWAY

Scene along the Haines Highway.
J.M. JANIS COLLECTION

Haines Cutoff Road

The Haines Cutoff road was authorized by the United States Army in November 1942 as the Alaska Pioneer Road was being finished. The cutoff was to be built to link the port of Haines, Alaska, with the Alaska Highway, a distance of 160 miles. It was also built to provide an alternative route to the highway in case the White Pass and Yukon Railway was blocked, to provide another port for the shipment of supplies to the highway, and to provide a possible mass evacuation route from Alaska in case that became necessary.

The road took almost one year to build—from January to December 1943—at a cost of over $13 million. The road traverses the rugged country on the east side of the St. Elias Range through parts of Alaska, British Columbia and the Yukon Territory.

Some of the same construction difficulties encountered on the Alaska Highway were also met on the Cutoff road, but much had been learned on the original pioneer road. Camps were built along the route for the construction workers. Major camps were at 103 mile and at Dezadeash Lake.

In the winter of 1944, the United States Army discontinued the winter maintenance of the road, and the Canadian portion was returned to the Canadian Army after the end of the war.

Ft. William H. Seward, near Haines, was built during 1902-04 under the supervision of Capt. Wilds P. Richardson. In 1922 the post was renamed Chilkoot Barracks. The first garrison (1904) consisted of Companies A-B-C and Field and Staff members, 3rd Infantry. At the start of World War II it was the only active military post in Alaska, manned with two companies of the 4th Infantry. The post was abandoned in 1953. The site now is called Port Chilkoot and has been turned into a major area tourist attraction. ASL FREDERICK ORDWAY PHOTO

Scenes of Haines during the war. UAA LULU FAIRBANKS COLLECTION 68-69-1188 & J.M. JANIS COLLECTION

City Hall in Haines.
J.M. JANIS COLLECTION

Constructing the Haines Highway. BILL HEBERT COLLECTION

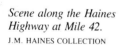

Scene along the Haines Highway at Mile 42.
J.M. HAINES COLLECTION

Contractor's camp north of Haines.
J.M. HAINES COLLECTION

28 Mile camp at -20 degrees F.
BILL HEBERT COLLECTION

Indian village of Klukwan, Alaska, along the route of the Haines Highway.
BILL HEBERT COLLECTION

Wells, north of Haines on the Chilkat River.
BILL HEBERT COLLECTION

The contractors on the Haines Highway faced the same hard winter conditions as on the Alaska Highway.
BILL HEBERT COLLECTION

Alaska Road Commission headquarters on the Chilkat River north of Haines. BILL HEBERT COLLECTION

12

RECONSTRUCTION

The reconstruction of the pioneer road was completed at this spot on Oct. 13, 1943 by the Utah Construction Company, one of many private contractors working for the Public Roads Administration. NA 30-N-44-873

Yukon Adventure

EXTENSION OF REMARKS

Hon. Homer D. Angell

of Oregon

in the House of Representatives

Thursday, March 2, 1944

Mr. Angell. Mr. Speaker, pursuant to authority heretofore granted, I am including as a part of these remarks an article entitled "Yukon Adventure," written by Capt. Richard L. Neuberger, aide-de-camp of General O'Connor, of the Northwest Service Command. This article appeared in the Saturday Evening Post in the issue of February 19, 1944. Captain Neuberger served with General O'Connor throughout much of the momentous history-making months while the Army engineers as well as the Public Roads Department were forging ahead, building the 1,600-mile highway through the bleak northland, connecting continental United States with central Alaska. This road will be known in history as one of the great adventures of road construction as a military project.

This article vividly portrays to us the hardships encountered by these brave men of our fighting forces who were detailed to this work, as well as the civilian employees who carried on where the Army left off, through temperatures varying from 90 degrees above to 60 below. These men relentlessly forced through a wild, bleak wilderness in the northland a modern highway within a short period of approximately a year. I am sure that every Member of Congress will not only be intensely interested but will be made acquainted with the effectiveness of our armed forces in military highway construction by reading this informative article. The article to which I refer is as follows:

> Yukon Adventure – Army Life in America's Bitterest Corner, Where Motors Freeze While Running, Tight Shoes Mean Amputated Feet, and Ice Forms Inside a Bottle of Whisky
>
> (By Capt. Richard L. Neuberger)

For a couple of fellows from the great Southwest, where a mere 32° above zero is cause for a meeting of the Hot Stove League, Lt. Boyd Pestotnik and Sgt. Philip Robichaud were in a cold spot. The motor in their carry-all had been quavering ominously for half an hour, and finally it had frozen fast on the Alaska Highway, 21 miles from the nearest Army camp.

Under ordinary circumstances, 21 miles is not a long way. But it is as far as 100, or even 1,000, when a Yukon winter clutches the land in its fiercest grip. Pestotnik came from Tulsa, Okla., and was wearing long underwear for the first time in his life. The sergeant was new to subzero temperatures, too. In fact, not in his 35 years in San Antonio, Tex., had he ever seen the thermometer drop to zero, let alone below it.

But the thermometer was below zero now. How much below, the two stranded Army men did not know. All they knew was that the cold clawed at them like a beast of prey. It seared their faces and bit their ears with invisible fangs. In the gathering gloom of the early Yukon afternoon, it was an unseen foe against which

G. I. parkas and woolen underwear were now their first line of defense. The young officer from Tulsa and the noncom from San Antonio might have felt even colder had they known that at that particular moment the Canadian meteorologist at Mayo, the nearest weather station, was writing "67° below zero" in his report for the day.

The problem confronting the pair from America's sunny Southwest was one of survival. Their vehicle had quit for keeps. They did not dare remove their fur mittens to tinker with the machinery. Darkness was muffling the wilderness. No other vehicles would brave the blast that night. Too late, they realized they should not have fared forth themselves. Without snowshoes, they could not leave the highway to forage for firewood. The heater had quit along with the motor. The carryall was a virtual refrigerator, but few refrigerators ever had been so frigid. The car offered some protection against the wind, but the cold – practically 100° below the freezing point – seeped through doors and windows like a deadly gas.

"We better start hiking," the sergeant said. "We'll freeze to death if we stay here. We gotta keep moving. Otherwise we're finished. I never would have believed it could get so cold anywhere this side of the moon."

Pestotnik was trying to remember what Handford, the square-shouldered mounted police constable back at Burwash Landing, had said when he saw Pestotnik's eider-down G. I. sleeping bag with its double layers. The words were coming back to him. "Lieutenant," the scarlet-jacketed mountie had said, "this is the best sleeping bag I ever saw. It'll be your best friend if you ever get stuck in a Yukon monsoon. Lieutenant, a Yukon monsoon is cold enough to freeze the blood in a musk ox's veins. But you just get into this sleeping bag and sleep it out. You may get awful darn hungry, but in this sleeping bag the frost will never nip you."

Now the lieutenant assumed command. "We stay here," he decided. "Take our sleeping bags out from under the back seat. We'll sleep 'er out, like Handford said."

With fingers already stiff, the two Americans marooned in a sea of frigidity unzipped their sleeping bags and crawled in. The hard seats of the carryall pinched their backs and corrugated their legs. But they were warm, and eventually they slept.

They were still in the sleeping bags at noon the next day when a pair of Army trucks poked out of the storm and took them to the camp along Beaver Creek and a pot-roast dinner, 21 miles away. At the station hospital at Whitehorse down the highway, Maj. Mendel Silverman looked them over. There were no chilblains, no frostbite, no nipped lungs. They were intact. Ninety-nine degrees below the freezing point, and their G.

I. sleeping bags had brought them through.

This was when we began to think we might have the Arctic licked. A couple of cheechakos from the balmy Southwest had survived the worst Yukon weather in 3 decades.

When the route for the 1,592-mile Alaska International Highway was first selected, veteran Army men had looked at the map with some misgivings. The job would mean stationing American soldiers in the coldest patches of North America. Year after year Alaska's lowest temperatures are always recorded at Tanana Crossing, and the highway goes straight through it. Canada's gaunt and lonely Yukon Territory has frozen and maimed more men than any other Arctic region, and the highway twists across the Yukon for 551 wilderness miles.

In such a land it was inevitable that trucks would freeze, bulldozers would be immobilized by ice, and manifolds and differentials and carburetors would fail to function. But what about the soldiers? This was the Army's dominant concern. Could recruits from Florida and Mississippi and southern California come unscathed through a Yukon winter?

During the last great influx into the Yukon, that of the Klondike gold rush in 1898, men had died along the trail every day during December, January, and February. Frost-bitten lungs and frozen limbs had sent scores of others back to Seattle and Edmonton crippled wrecks. The trek to Whitehorse and Dawson was studded with pain, and men caught by the kind of weather which snared Lieutenant Pestotnik and Sergeant Robichaud often were not found until the thaw of the following spring.

The present Yukon migration rivals the one of '98. Approximately 20,000 soldiers have worked on the Alaska Highway and such associated projects as telephone lines, barracks, and landing strips. Construction of the road commenced in April of 1942. Today soldiers are driving trucks its full length, from Dawson Creek on the British Columbia plains to Fairbanks in the heart of Alaska.

In that time, with 20,000 men – many of whom had never felt even freezing temperatures before – working out in the open in the coldest part of North America, there has been only one death from exposure.

In addition, Col. Walter F. von Zelinski, surgeon of the Army's Northwest Service Command, has said, "We have treated 140 men who were incapacitated by the cold. Of those 140 cases, all except 4 recovered completely, with no ill effects. The 4 required amputations of 2 or less toes. No amputations of hands or feet were necessary.

"In my opinion," Colonel von Zelinski has added, "this constitutes an all-time record for protection of the human body in the coldest imaginable temperatures. The record becomes all the more remarkable when one considers that three regiments of Negro soldiers, composed almost wholly of men who never had been out of the deep South, played an important role in the construction of the Alaska Highway."

THE LESSONS OF MOUNT M'KINLEY

Colonel von Zelinski attributes this showing to three major factors: "First, the cold-weather discipline instilled in the troops, in the form of repeated instructions for behavior and living in extreme cold. Second, the studies made by the Army for safeguarding our personnel in temperatures touching 70 degrees below zero. And third, the excellent Arctic clothing and unsurpassed sleeping equipment which have resulted from those studies."

The Quartermaster Corps of the Army was ready for the great road-building adventure in the far north long before that adventure began. On the 20,300-foot summit of Mount McKinley, loftiest spot on the continent, Bradford Washburn conducted special clothing experiments for the Quartermaster General. Washburn is one of the best known mountain climbers in North America. He also is director of the New England Museum of Natural History.

"I believe Mount McKinley is the coldest point in the world which men can reach," Washburn told Maj. Gen. Edmund B. Gregory, Quartermaster General of the United States Army.

It was on McKinley's frigid crest that Washburn discovered that blankets and quilts, no matter how numerous, are a frail reed against extreme cold, and that a sleeping bag is essential. There he found that eider down is warmer than any other material as a filling for the bag. He also found that a smaller sack fitting within the outer bag provided considerably more protection than a single bag of double thickness. And he insisted that the bag be made light enough for a man to carry with ease. "We don't want soldiers getting separated from their equipment," he warned.

Along the full length of the Alaska Highway's 1,592 miles—at truck relay station, airport, and signal unit—the G. I. sleeping bag is the most popular as well as the most vital article of equipment. I have eaten in a tent so cold that canned corn froze in my mess kit and I dared not take off my gloves, yet that night I slept as snug as in a steam-heated hotel room. The G. I. sleeping bag bridged the temperature gap. When he came to the opening of the Alaska Highway, Maj. Gen. George R. Pearkes, wearer of the Victoria Cross and commander of Canada's Pacific Army Command, told Brig. Gen. James A. (Patsy) O'Connor, who heads the Northwest Service Command, that the American Army's sleeping bag was the best piece of Arctic equipment he ever had seen.

This was the voice of authority, for as a young man in 1913 Pearkes had been a Mountie constable at Dalton Post on the Alaskan border. And when the Canadian general left Whitehorse he had in the pocket of his battle dress all the specifications of our G. I. sleeping bags for his own army to study.

The tendency of our soldiers at the start of their Arctic service was to wear too many clothes. This sounds paradoxical, but one of the facts definitely established by Bradford Washburn and his associates in the cold-weather tests was that perspiration and overheating are the gravest perils to a man on the northern trail. It is practically second nature for a soldier, especially if

he has come straight from an orange-blossom climate, to wrap everything around himself except the kitchen linoleum when he feels the temperature falling to 60 below.

This is where Colonel von Zelinski's "cold-weather discipline" enters the situation. Our soldiers along the Alaska Highway have been schooled against dressing too heavily. All of them have been warned that men freeze to death when their inner clothing, becoming saturated with moisture from perspiration, conducts the heat from the body and then freezes hard. Another maxim hammered home is that several layers of light clothing are infinitely warmer than single layer of equal weight. And no soldier is allowed to wear tight shoes or breeches that pinch at the knee. "Tight shoes mean frozen feet" is virtually an aphorism all the way from Dawson Creek to Fairbanks.

When the American Army moved into the Yukon nearly 2 years ago, it found a military organization on the scene which had endured Arctic winters for almost half a century. It was a small organization, but its experience and knowledge could be applied to the Army's thousands. This was the Royal Canadian Mounted Police. From the Mounties our troops have learned much. "No leather on the feet after the thermometer hits 10 above" is a Mountie rule, and the American Army follows it too. Both organizations recommend rubber shoe packs between 10 above and zero.

When the temperature is well below zero, fur mukluks or fabric galoshes generously stuffed with socks are standard footgear. "In extreme cold," says General O'Connor, the commander of the first United States military force in the Yukon, "soldiers must wear galoshes large enough to contain two pairs of light wool socks, a pair of heavy knitted wool socks, a jute foot sock, and an insole of felt. Evergreen needles stuffed into the shoe outside the socks is extra insulating material. But our main emphasis is on having the cold-weather footgear fit loosely. The feet are the part of the body most vulnerable to abnormally low temperatures. Tight footgear cuts off circulation, stimulates perspiration, and invites freezing."

Patrols as far north as the polar sea have taught the Mounties many tricks of travel in the Arctic. Now these tricks are saving American as well as Canadian lives. Dog sleds have been used by our soldiers in running surveys and carrying out reconnaissance missions. Capt. William Hammond, of the Twenty-ninth Engineer Battalion, mushed 560 miles across the Mackenzie Mountains from Whitehorse to Fort Norman, but first he asked the Mounties how they would keep alive on such a trek. Throughout his equipment and around the sled, on their advice, he scattered big blocks of sulfur. If his hands froze too stiff to grip a match, he could always use wrists and palms to ignite the blocks. He also carried a pail of oil-soaked rags. Perhaps survival might depend upon getting a fire started quickly. If you break through a hidden spring on the trail, it requires only a few minutes for wet legs to freeze. And around his neck on a blue lanyard he hung his G. I. mittens of wolfskin. Once laid down, the mittens might never be picked up again by fingers rapidly stiffening at 70 below. The lanyard was assurance that the mittens would always be available. It was 70 below and winds scoured the Mackenzie passes, but Hammond completed his mission and returned by dog sled, too, a total journey of more than

1,100 miles across unexplored terrain.

Meat and vegetables had to be thawed in an oven before being cooked. Seasoned lumber which had been outdoors froze, too, and would not take a nail, but split into kindling at the first stroke of the hammer. I saw soldiers starting trucks by building bonfires under the differentials and waving blowtorches over the spark plugs and cylinder heads. It was common practice to coax bulldozers into action in the morning with huge, roaring fires beneath the treads and engines. Frequently truck convoys were accompanied by a steam caboose. This was a truck at the end carrying a small boiler, fed with wood from along the road, which could generate live steam. Wielding stream hoses, the crew of the caboose could thaw out the other vehicles of the convoy. When the thermometer stood at 66 below on the Donjek River, near the Alaska-Yukon international line, truck motors froze up while going at full speed in low gear. One of the first freezing points was the line between the gasoline tank and the carburetor. Each truck driver carried a small hand pump to open the gas line, but frequently the cold which froze the line paralyzed unmittened hands before the pump could be put to use.

"Mittens are much warmer than gloves," read the instructions to soldiers along the Alaska Highway. "Fingers numbed from cold completely impair a soldier's efficiency, and gloves warm enough for habitual wear are too bulky for the proper handling of instruments and weapons." Immobilized fingers were the greatest obstacle to the repair of trucks, aircraft, and bulldozers. I have seen a heroic Air Corps mechanic at the Whitehorse Airport require nearly an hour to screw a small nut on the back of a transport-plane engine. With his face muffled in scarfs against a 56-below wind, he would warm the nut at the heater of a nearby jeep, so that it would not stick to the flesh. Then he would hurriedly pull off his heavy mittens, run up the ladder to the engine and try to start the nut in place. But his fingers would freeze into immobility too soon. He could not get the nut adjusted quickly enough. Eighteen times he repeated the procedure, warming his hands over and over again at the jeep engine. On the nineteenth attempt he was able to get the nut started on the bolt before his fingers stiffened. Then he put on his mittens and tightened it with a wrench.

This is what temperatures can do in the coldest part of North America—and it actually is colder along the strip served by the Alaska Highway than 500 miles northward on the Arctic Ocean. When it was 55 below at Tanana Crossing and 57 below at Whitehorse last winter, it was a mere 47 below at Aklavik, where the Mackenzie piles its delta on the shores of the Beaufort Sea. Point Barrow is seldom as cold as Tanana Crossing. Grease and oil in Army trucks and planes at Tanana froze as hard as ice. Many shivering pilots had to start their aircraft by attaching a rope to one of the blades of the propeller and winding the other end around the hub of a truck.

MEN AGAINST THE NORTH

The cold did strange things and created strange problems. We cracked open eggs to find crystals of ice inside the shell. Potatoes became so ribbed with frozen strips that they looked like Italian marble. Jean Louis Coudert, Catholic bishop of the Yukon, and a veteran of many years in the Arctic, visiting Army camps along the Alaska Highway, watched a hot dinner freeze on his plate as he rushed the 120 feet from the kitchen to the mess tent. I can vouch for the fact that chunks of ice were floating in my shaving lotion one morning when the mercury touched 61 degrees below. Water pipes buried far beneath the ground split apart in weather like this. The water in 85-proof Scotch whisky froze into lumps which floated in the alcohol, although 100-proof retained its liquid form in toto.

One difficulty never licked was that of frozen culverts along the highway. Ice would plug these as tightly shut as a corked bottle and the rampant creek would pile a glacier of ice on the road. The highway patrol would come along with oil drums and build a big fire to thaw out the culvert, but in an hour or so it would be plugged once more.

At Whitehorse, headquarters of the Northwest Service Command, the Army had to build virtual barns over its water tanks and put stoves inside. Dawson had to heat the entire city water supply with electric coils and wood stand-by boilers from October until March. In each house and building, a 3/8-inch valve of hot water was drained into sewer pipes to keep the sewage system open during the winter months. And throughout the coldest weather of December and January, when it was 70 below along the White and Donjek and Duke Rivers, the antifreeze solution for trucks and bulldozers actually froze hard in the containers. Officers of unimpeachable integrity have made affidavit to this, when questioned by skeptics.

The Northwest Service Command commenced operations in an old C.C.C. building. Offices were at the front. We slept in a long hall at the rear. General O'Connor's office was barely large enough for a plywood desk and a chair. Most of the time our plumbing was frozen. The building faced toward the Whitehorse Rapids on the Yukon River, where once Jack London had boated outfits through the roughest stretch of water on the way to the Klondike. The Yukon River watershed, commencing at Whitehorse and including Mayo, Selkirk, Dawson, Tanana Crossing, and Northway, is probably as cold as any region inhabited by man except northern Siberia. This was the scene of London's famous story To Build a Fire, the tale of a cheechako who lost his life when snow sliding off a spruce tree quenched his campfire. Many of our soldiers have read that story, and none of them will ever build a fire beneath an evergreen laden with snow. It is not uncommon for the temperature to be a maximum of 50 degrees below from Whitehorse to Tanana for 2 weeks without relief.

Our Army's equipment and personnel suffered cruel punishment during such periods. But all emphasis was put upon the safety of the men. If abandoning a truck piled with ice meant saving a driver's life or limbs,

then the truck was abandoned. Vehicles moved on the most savage winter days, but not at the expense of human life. The sole casualty due to a winter unparalleled in brutality even for Alaska and the Yukon was a Negro truck driver whose vehicle failed on the Slana cut-off in Alaska. Brush and cleared-away timber slashings enabled him to build a fire alongside the road. Had he stuck by the fire, eventually he would have been picked up and rescued. But he decided to walk the 14 miles to camp. It was a fatal decision. He froze to death on the way. The temperature was 66° below zero that afternoon.

Three of the seven regiments engaged in the pioneer construction of the Alaska Highway—the Ninety-third, the Ninety-fifth, and the Ninety-seventh Engineers—were made up of colored troops. Most of these Negro soldiers had never before been out of the South. The bulk of them had yet to see a thermometer register zero, let alone half a hundred degrees below zero. How did they survive the Yukon winter?

"The Negro troops have distinguished themselves," reported Col. John W. Wheeler, former Indiana highway commissioner, and then engineer in charge of the Alaska Highway. "Of the 1,592 miles of road, they have built about 460. Working under the severe handicap of extreme cold and moving ahead so rapidly that their living quarters were primitive and sketchy, they have nevertheless constructed a road through some of the most rugged wilderness on the North American continent. The morale of the Negro battalions has been good. From the health records, it appears that they have withstood well the rigors of the far North. The interest they have displayed in the task is remarkable. And they are top-notch cooks. Some of the best meals on the road have been served in their camps. I believe biscuits with country gravy constitute their favorite dish."

After studying health records and medical reports, Colonel von Zelinski has declared that the colored troops suffered no more than their white comrades from such cold-weather maladies as arthritis, rheumatism, and respiratory infections. "In fact," the colonel has added, "there were comparatively few colds all along the road. It is possible that the extremely low temperatures reduced the virulence of the cold virus."

Yet, in sickness or in health, everyone came to appreciate just plain honest-to-goodness warmth. Outdoors at almost 100° below the freezing point, your face feels as if it were being branded with a hot iron. Knees encased in woolen underwear quaver involuntarily. Feet tingle painfully and then become numb. One yearns for warmth, whatever the source of the warmth may be. Col. K. B. Bush, Northwest Service Command chief of staff, came to duty in the Yukon straight from Lt. Gen., then Maj. Gen., George S.

Patton's staff at Desert Training Center in Indio, Calif. He said his idea of heaven was to be as close to an oil stove as one could get without being burned alive.

THAWING OUT

And I remember the colored staff sergeant who grinned at me as we sat in a pyramidal tent on opposite sides of a glowing little wood stove that had been fashioned from a discarded oil drum. Outside, a 50-below wind swept down from the St. Elias Mountains—loftiest range in Canada. "Ah's happy, lieutenant," the sergeant said, " 'cause ah's warm."

We felt somewhat more comfortable when Colonel Wheeler wrote us from India, where he was on a new assignment, and said that 66 below was considerably more bearable than 146 above, but we also wished we could devise a way to trade weather back and forth with him and thus ameliorate both extremes.

Construction companies hiring men to build installations and facilities along the highway have warned their prospective employees what conditions they may face. One sign gave this advance notice:

"THIS IS NO PICNIC
"Working and living conditions on this job are as difficult as those encountered on any construction job ever done in the United States or foreign territory.
"Men hired on this job will be required to work and live under the most extreme conditions imaginable. The temperature will range from 90° above zero to 70° below zero. Men will have to fight swamps, rivers, ice, and cold. Mosquitoes, flies, and gnats will not only be annoying but will cause bodily harm. If you are not prepared to work under these and similar conditions, do not apply.
"BECHTEL-PRICE-CALLAHAN."

The sign does not exaggerate. Ordinary pleasures and sensations, taken for granted by all of us as civilians, are viewed from a new perspective after a Yukon winter. I remember how it felt to get to the States at last. I was riding on a train between Vancouver, British Columbia, and Seattle. We were 3 hours late. My fellow passengers had commenced to grumble loudly. They damned the railroad company, the Government, and all things in general. I looked around me. The parlor car was warm. The seat I was sitting in was soft and comfortable. Along the track, the lush green of the Puget Sound lowland was a welcome contrast to the endless miles of ice and snow. Across the aisle, the pretty brunette with trim legs looked all right too. I glanced up ahead toward the dining car. I had just had my first glass of fresh milk in 5 months. I knew there was more where that had come from. I pushed back my shoulders and again felt the delicious warmth of the parlor car. Me? I didn't care if the train rolled on forever.

The first truck to bring mail from Dawson Creek, B.C., to Fairbanks, Alaska, December 1943. USA SC 323034

This is what the PRA encountered on the highway in 1943: mud, ruts and in many places, washouts, slides and miles of no road at all. Realignment was a necessity in many places from the original pioneer road. NA 30-N-42-1960

The U.S. Army controlled all traffic on the highway, a military necessity but a nuisance to the civilian contractors. The top photo shows a control point on the Richardson Highway in Alaska. The bottom photo is a control point at Whitehorse, both in 1944. USA SC 254436 & NA 111-SC-571409

"Rusty" Dow, legendary highway driver

Obituary by Dalene Perrigo in the June 20, 1989, Anchorage Times.

Benzie Ola "Rusty" Dow traded her career as a truck driver for that of an artist in the early 1960s and although the second career was as successful as the first, she longed for the old days.

At a time when most women stayed at home, Mrs. Dow had developed a career in truck driving, a field dominated by men. A free spirit, this "redheaded ball of energy" at first took odd jobs that needed a truck and a good driver. From her arrival in 1934 until her death at age 95 on June 18, 1989, at the Valley Hospital in Palmer, Alaska, was home.

She came to Palmer the winter of 1934, just a few months before the Matanuska Valley colonists. Bringing her own ton-and-a-half Chevy truck, she put it to work when she received a contract to transfer mail from the railroad station to the post office, then started a trucking business and shopping service between Independence Mine, Palmer, and Anchorage. At the same time, she had a lease on the only laundry in town and ran a charter service to Anchorage, driving an old Oldsmobile four-door sedan.

It was while making a laundry run in March of 1939, that she met Russell Dow, a young miner, waiting for a lift to the mine. They married in December of the same year.

"I don't know when I learned to drive truck," she said in a 1979 interview. "I was just like any other Texas ranch girl. Driving was natural."

When World War II broke out, Mrs. Dow went to work for the quartermaster at Fort Richardson, and was later transferred to engineering under General Tally. She was his driver and ran errands in her job as "go-for."

One big assignment involved hauling supplies to various camps along the Alaska Highway, which made her the first woman to drive the newly constructed international roadway. It took two weeks from the time she left Anchorage until her return.

Because of her ability, she was selected for special assignments, such as driving Teddy Roosevelt's grandson through the Whittier tunnel to the railroad connection and back.

She gave up truck driving in 1960.

Painting was her third love, "after Russ and trucks." While in high school she studied art and at one time went to a summer workshop in Maine. She also taught at an art institute at a community college. Her realistic paintings range from moose and winter cabins, to portraits such as those of Abe Lincoln and Grandma Easi, an Eklutna Indian woman.

Not restricted to oils, her preference, she created art works in charcoal, pen and ink, watercolors and pastels. Trying other mediums, she gathered clay from the beach for sculptures, and made copper etchings.

Her works won prizes in many Alaska shows including Fur Rendezvous and for 15 years, she managed the art department at the Alaska State Fair in Palmer.

Born June 15, 1894, in Wallace Station, Austin County, Texas, she grew up on a farm in Texas, and did her share of picking cotton. When her brother Lanna Scott homesteaded at the end of Scott Road in Palmer, Rusty and her parents came north to help him prove-up on the homestead.

Rusty and Russ also homesteaded. In 1947 the couple moved into a small log building built by the Knik Bridge construction crew. This was home although Mrs. Dow's health began to fail in 1967 and by 1972, she was living in the Palmer Pioneers' Home.

THINGS
YOU SHOULD KNOW
about your trip and the
ALASKA HIGHWAY JOB

Acc # 88-56

ISSUED BY

E. W. ELLIOTT, General Contractor
SEATTLE, WASHINGTON

This pamphlet produced by the E.W. Elliott Company in 1943 tells what a prospective civilian employee would encounter. However, the extreme winter weather conditions and summer insect infestations could not be described adequately on paper—they would have to be experienced first-hand.

FOR VICTORY
BUY UNITED STATES SAVINGS BONDS AND STAMPS

A word about *your* future . . . .

This may be the last "big money" many of us will ever have a chance to make. It's a swell opportunity for you to lay aside some money against the time when you'll need it lots worse than you do now, and to safeguard yourself and your family against that rainy day. So for your own good we hope you'll save most of your wages and send the money home.

Put as much as you can into War Bonds and send the rest home. This is the best way we know for you to protect yourself, your family and your country.

You can make arrangements on the job to buy War Bonds through the company's payroll deduction plan. Under this plan you can have the amount you wish to save every week deducted from your pay check. When you have saved enough to purchase a bond, the company will buy it for you.

E. W. ELLIOTT
General Contractor

FORM P12 REV. 8-43

THE ALASKA HIGHWAY IS THE ROAD TO VICTORY

This company's work has to do with the building of the Alaska-Canada Military Highway and providing adequate facilities to make the road an important and effective military route. It is considered by most military men as a springboard for attack on Japan as well as an important defensive project in our plans to protect and defend Alaska. It is probably the country's No. 1 war job.

In order to qualify for work on this project you will have to comply with the following:

1. You must be a citizen of the United States and be able to furnish adequate proof of your citizenship in the form of a birth certificate, naturalization papers, army or navy discharge papers, baptismal record or some other document which proves who you are and where you were born.

2. If you are registered in Selective Service, you must get written permission from your local Draft Board to leave the United States for a period of at least six months. This draft clearance is called Form 351 and the company will help you get the release. You must not now be employed in Essential War Industry or if you are so employed you must have a release without prejudice from such work from your last employer, or a certificate of availability from your local United States Employment Service.

3. You must have an adequate supply of winter clothes so that you will be able to work outside during the cold months.

4. If the job for which you are applying requires tools, you will have to furnish them. Personal tools are used at your own risk. If you want them protected against loss you will have to arrange for your own insurance.

5. You must furnish the company with your Social Security number.

6. You are required to pass a physical examination to determine your fitness for work, submit to the necessary innoculations, sign the employment contract and carry out the other steps in the hiring procedure which the Government has set up for us to follow. The age limit is 62 years.

If you are willing to accept employment on this basis, if you are a good workman and want to help your country, you will probably be able to get a job. We do not, however, employ anyone who is not willing to put up with considerable personal discomfort, hardship, and tough living conditions, if necessary, in order to get this job completed. Also, if you should be asked to work, temporarily, at some job other than the one for which you have been hired, you will be expected to do so. For such other work you will be paid your regular rate of pay as stated in your employment agreement.

THESE ARE THE THINGS YOU SHOULD KNOW ABOUT THE JOB

The following regulations apply, equally, to all persons employed by us for work in Alaska and/or Canada. Some apply only to those who go to the job site and beyond by rail or truck. They are mostly government or military rules set up for your protection and must be observed in all details by everyone. It will save you a lot of unnecessary confusion and inconvenience if you understand them thoroughly before you leave.

Birth Certificate: Be sure and carry your birth certificate or some other definite written proof of your birth on your person when you leave for the job. A voter's registration card, army or navy discharge papers, baptismal record, or affidavit from the county clerk at the place of your birth is acceptable, if you are native born. You will need this in order to pass the Canadian Immigration requirements and to re-enter the U. S. If there is any question in your mind about your proof of citizenship be sure to ask the person who employs you to check your papers and make sure that they are in order.

Naturalized Citizens: If you are a naturalized citizen of the U. S. you must furnish the company with your certificate number when you are hired and carry the certificate with you as proof of your citizenship. This is necessary, not only to comply with the immigration laws of the U. S. and Canada, but also because under the terms of our contract we are only to employ American citizens for this particular job. The affidavit of citizenship which you are required to sign is our evidence of this fact and becomes a part of the Company record. If you are leaving from Seattle and have been passed by the Alaska Travel Control, please remember that your permit to enter Alaska is not considered proper proof of citizenship.

Draft Deferments: If you are registered under the Selective Service Act you must secure permission from your draft board to leave the United States for a period of six months to work on this job, before we can employ you. This release, Form 351, is issued to you by your local draft board upon your application and to help you get it, the Company gives you a letter to use as proof that you actually have a job on the Alaska Highway project. It should be issued in duplicate, one copy for the Company records and one copy for you to carry with you while you are in our employ. If all arrangements for your release have been made but the form has not been issued at your scheduled time of departure, arrangements can be made to forward your copy to you upon its arrival in our office. This will enable you to leave for the job without delay. If you quit or are terminated by the Company, and return home before the expiration of this deferment, we are required to immediately inform your draft board and ask them to cancel your release.

Physical Fitness: Alaska is a rugged place and it takes men who are physically fit to do the job. If there is anything wrong with you physically, mentally or morally this country will bring it out. You will have to take a physical examination at the Company's expense, because we must know whether or not you are qualified to do the work for which you are being considered, as much for your protection and welfare as for our own. If you are not in good shape, don't try to hide it, because it will only mean that you will have to come home, at your own expense, too. All employees must take typhoid and smallpox innoculations before departure or after arrival on the job. If you commence or complete innoculations before departure be sure and take your innoculation record card with you.

Fire Arms: You cannot take guns to Canada without a special permit. You can get this permit by application to the Commissioner, Canadian Mounted Police at Ottawa, Canada. If you do not have a permit before you leave for the job, you had better leave your guns at home, as they will probably be confiscated by Canadian Customs officials at the border. At the present time there is no law that prohibits your taking firearms into Alaska. However, Alaska is a war zone, and to be on the safe side, we suggest that you leave guns at home. After you are on the job, perhaps you can arrange with local authorities for a permit, and your gun can be mailed to you if you must have it. Assuming you have the necessary permits or authority to take firearms along, turn them over to the master of the vessel when you go aboard. They will be returned to you in good order when your voyage is ended.

Liquor: You are not permitted to have liquor in your possession while a passenger on any vessel operated by E. W. Elliott. The captain is required to take up any liquor which you have before you can board the vessel. Liquor is confiscated by the authorities upon your entry into Alaska or Canada, any way, so there's not much point in taking any with you. If you want to do a good job and get along with the other fellows—DON'T DRINK! Excessive drinking on the part of any E. W. Elliott employee is considered just cause for immediate dismissal.

Exposed Film: If you have exposed negatives with you, they must be turned over to the Customs authorities at the point of

—3—

departure or at the border. Customs will send them to a commercial photographer to be developed and printed, and after the prints have been censored, they will be forwarded to you together with the negatives upon payment of the customary charge for this service. This rule also applies to negatives in cameras, whether or not the complete roll has been exposed.

Photos: Any photographs in your possession must be submitted to the Customs officials for censoring at the time of your departure.

Maps: Do not take maps with you that show details relative to harbors, coastal and defense areas. They will be picked up by the Customs before you sail.

Cameras, Binoculars, Flashlights, Radios, Electric Razors, Etc.: If you are taking any of these items, be sure and check them with the master or purser of your ship when you go aboard. They will be returned to you in good order when you reach your destination. As far as cameras are concerned, you can take them, but there is always the risk of having them picked up at any time by the authorities.

Clothing: If you are properly clothed, you can work out in very bitter weather without too much inconvenience. It won't be pleasant, but it will be bearable. Therefore, it is absolutely essential that you have the necessary winter clothing. At Whitehorse and vicinity it may be 50 degrees below or even colder during the winter months. Anything can happen in this country and the right kind of clothing will make a big difference.

In the spring, mosquitoes are a problem. This can be solved to a certain degree by a liberal use of mosquito netting for head nets which the Company furnishes. During the summer it probably will get hot during the day but the nights are cool. In general we'll say this about the climate; it's awfully tough in the winter, the spring months are not so bad, in the summer and fall working conditions are ideal.

As far as clothing is concerned, you won't go far wrong if you observe the following:

Wool garments are absolutely essential; be sure and take some waterproof or water repellant clothes, too. Take along woolen underwear, the two-piece variety is best, leather gloves, woolen shirts, lots of wool socks, and a parka or sheepskin coat if possible. You'll need a warm cap that covers your ears, extra work shoes or shoe packs, large enough to fit after you put on a couple

—4—

of pairs of sox and use insoles. Overshoes and felt boots will come in handy, too. and are probably the most satisfactory type of footwear for this country. We recommend that you take wool liners for your gloves and cap, and, if possible, "tin pants." These can be worn over regular wool pants and will help, not only to keep you dry, but will act as a windbreak as well. For summer work. regular work clothes will do.

Take all your clothing from the States. You may not be able to buy any on the job, and remember, if you are not well clothed you'll probably have to come home before you get well started.

Personal Baggage: Baggage is not restricted to any definite amount, but since space is at a premium, both while traveling and in the camp, it is a good idea to limit yourself to essential equipment. Bedding is furnished by the Company, and since you have only to bring clothing, personal effects, and tools required for your work, there should be ample room for everything you need. We recommend that you take extra towels and soap, too. If you have more than one piece of baggage, you will find it handy to pack your personal effects, razor, tooth brush, towel, etc., in a small bag or package. You can keep this with you in your stateroom or berth while traveling and check the rest of your baggage.

Transportation: The Company pays your transportation from the place you are hired to your point of employment on the job. You will also be furnished traveling expenses at the rate of $2.50 per day for meals and $2.50 per day for lodgings while you are traveling, except when such meals and lodging are furnished by the Company. In this case you do not receive traveling expenses for the period covered. Payment of your traveling expense allowance will either be made in Seattle prior to your departure for Alaska or after your arrival on the project.

In addition you will be allowed wages during the period you are traveling to the job. Your wages will be figured on the basis of eight hours straight time per day from the date and hour of your departure until arrival on the project but are limited to a maximum of forty hours per week during each regularly established work week, that is Monday through Sunday. Travel time wages except in special cases will not be paid immediately after your arrival on the job, but will be paid off at some time not less than two nor more than four weeks after you have commenced work on the project.

If you stick it out until your contract is completed, that is for nine months, or if we find it necessary to send you home before

—5—

this time through no fault of your own, we pay your transportation and traveling expenses back to the point where you were hired. You will also be paid travel time wages up to a maximum of forty hours per week during each regularly established work week and you will get the same traveling expense allowance that you receive when you are traveling to the job. Arrangements for settlement and payment of these amounts will be made at the time you leave the project and your checks will be mailed from the Seattle Office after the necessary papers have been received and properly audited by us.

If you quit, though, or if you are discharged for good cause before your contract is completed, you pay your own way home. To cover this possibility the Company is required by the Government to withhold a certain amount each week from your wages until we have accumulated the minimum cost of your fare home, or back to the nearest point of entry in the United States. Actually this is your money and if you leave before your employment contract is completed, we use it to buy your transportation back to the United States.

This matter is covered fully in the employment contract which you must sign. If it isn't absolutely clear, ask us to explain further. The amount of your transportation withholding varies, depending on where you are going to work and on your point of recruitment. The man who hires you will be glad to tell you how much will be withheld in your particular case and how it will be used.

Settlement of Transportation Withholding: If you are working at Whitehorse and vicinity and terminate your employment voluntarily or are fired for just cause, the cost of your return transportation to the United States will be deducted from the amount of your withholding and a statement of any balance due given you. Upon receipt of this statement at our Seattle Office you will be mailed a check for any balance you have coming. It is well to remember that if transportation cannot be arranged for you on one of our own ships, you will be required to pay your way out via commercial transport. If your contract has been completed, your transportation will be paid by the Company back to the place you were employed, and you will be refunded the entire amount of your withholding from Seattle when we receive the statement of account which is given you before you leave the job.

Wages and Hours: The following wage and hour conditions apply to all employees of the E. W. Elliott Company who work on the Alaska-Canada Highway Project. These provisions have been established by Government agencies, not the Company, and

—6—

must be agreed to by you as a conditions of employment. You are paid in accordance with the Public Roads Administration wage scale for your work.

If you work in Canadian territory and are employed on an hourly basis it is an eight-hour five-day week at straight time with time-and-on-half for all hours over eight in any one day or over forty hours in any one work-week. If you are hired on a straight weekly or monthly salary, you get paid regardless—but do not get overtime, since allowances for it have been included in computing your wage.

If you work in Alaska, it is an eight-hour five-day week at straight time with time-and-one-half for all hours over eight in any one day or over forty in any one work-week, with this exception—you get double-time for work performed on the seventh consecutive day of your work-week.

Weekly or monthly employees hired on straight salary basis do not get overtime because it has already been included in computing their salaries.

Usually you get plenty of overtime. Shifts customarily run ten hours, but because of weather conditions, shortages of vital materials, and so forth, this may not always be the case. There will probably be some times during the long summer days when you will work more than 10 hours a day. In any event if you are willing and able to work, you are guaranteed payment of an amount equivalent to forty hours at straight time in any one work-week in both Alaska and Canada, even though conditions on the job make it impossible for the work to be performed. Other than this, there is no guarantee on hours of work.

Travel time going to and from camp to job locations up to one-half hour each way per day is not considered pay time. If it takes you longer than one-half hour to get from camp to the place you are working, you will be paid regular wages for such excess time, both going and coming back to camp.

There is nothing in your employment contract that guarantees you any other job than the one for which you signed, and our employment agents, under no circumstances, have authority to make you any promise of a change in classification. There is always the chance, though, that changes in our operations or personnel requirements may provide an opening for you, and in this case if you are the right man for the job, you will probably get consideration.

—7—

Pay Checks: You are paid once a week by Company check on the job. The Company makes no allotments, so you will receive the full amount you have earned less any deductions required by law for board and room, War bonds, etc., and it will be up to you to send money home yourself. Company employees in our job offices will explain how you can do this and if necessary, help you make arrangements. If you work in Canadian territory, you will be paid in Canadian dollars, but allowances are made for exchange so the net result is just the same as though you were working in the United States. In other words, you are not penalized by the rate of exchange nor do you have to pay Canadian income taxes on what you make. The only exception in connection with changing your money into American dollars is a 1% excise tax charged by the Canadian Government, and if you should have occasion to do this, it is at your own expense.

To speed up delivery of your letters home we suggest that you send checks, money orders, etc., by registered mail.

Medical Aid and Compensation: Industrial Insurance is provided for you by the Company in accordance with the laws covering compensation that apply at the place you are working, and in case of injury, Army or Public Roads Administration doctors will probably be available to take care of you. At each camp the Company maintains a first-aid station and attendant to take care of "on the spot" injuries.

A medical aid and hospitalization plan for other than industrial accidents is available in the area and the cost is 40 cents U. S. per week. You can get complete information as to just how this medical plan applies to you and to what extent you are protected, at any of our job offices. You will have to sign up and the weekly fee will be deducted from your check.

All employees of E. W. Elliott who are U. S. citizens working on this project are protected under public law 208. Subject to certain terms and provisions, this law provides for payment of a death benefit not to exceed $7,500.00, plus $200.00 funeral expenses, should you be killed while in our employ. In the event of accidental injury incurred while you are working, the maximum rate of compensation is $25.00 per week, plus all necessary medical and hospital care. There is a waiting period of seven days after disabling accidents or sickness before compensation begins. If adequate facilities are available at the job site, you will be taken care of there. Otherwise, you will be taken at Company expense to the nearest place where good attention can be obtained. For further details as to just how this protection ap-

—8—

plies to you at the place you are working, ask at the job office, they will be able to supply the information. In the event that you are sent out for medical treatment, it is well to remember that you must bring written evidence from the examining doctor to this effect to support any claim you may have for travel expense or compensation.

After you have left our employ any communications concerning compensation or claims should be addressed to the United Pacific Insurance Company, Exchange Building, Seattle, Washington. This company is our insurance carrier and is responsible for settling and adjusting such matters with you.

All injuries or sickness no matter how slight must be reported immediately to your supervisor or to the job office so that report forms can be completed by the Company and forwarded to Seattle. Remember it's usually the little injuries not properly treated that develop into the most serious cases.

Living Conditions and Food: You may not like your living quarters. This is not like living at the Ritz. Most of our men, however, are quartered in barracks with hot and cold running water, adequate heat, and plumbing. Temporarily, you may have to live in tents. If you do, they'll be fairly warm and dry. The E. W. Elliott Company makes every effort to keep your quarters clean but in the final analysis this is pretty much up to you. Privacy is at a premium, but we like the men who work for us and we think you will too. If you're a "right guy," 'you'll get along fine. Whenever possible this Company will do what it can to improve the living quarters, but remember there's a war on and other more important things must necessarily come first.

As far as the food is concerned, we'll be surprised if it isn't the best you've ever eaten. The E. W. Elliott Company has a reputation throughout Alaska and Northern Canada for the kind of grub we serve. There's one thing you can count on—good food, and plenty of it. This, of course, assuming we can continue to get the food and transport it to the job locations. If at times we fall short, you can blame our enemies and continue to do what you can to lick them.

Board and Room: At the present time you are charged for board and room on the following basis: If you are working in Alaska, the deduction is $1.50 per day. If you are working in Canadian territory, the deduction is $1.25 per day. These rates, however, are subject to change without notice if we should be required by Government agencies to make some adjustment in

—9—

them. No deduction will be made for board and room for the days you are traveling either to the job or back to your point of employment upon completion of your contract.

Commissaries: The E. W. Elliott Company does not operate commissaries at the present time but arrangements have been made at most job locations so you can fill your ordinary needs for personal effects, tobacco, drugs, and some clothing items, through commissaries operated by other contractors who are working in this area. The cost should be reasonable. It is possible, however, that stocks may be very limited, so we suggest you take a good supply of everything you will need with you. Purchases made at these commissaries must be for cash, as the Company makes no salary deductions for such purchases. There are private stores, also, but usually their stocks are very limited, and prices high.

Tobacco: Tobacco and cigarettes are not sold aboard Company vessels. If your destination is Whitehorse, you'd better take smoking material to last you five or six days. You'll be able to buy what you need in this line at commissaries on the job or in private stores. If the commissaries are well stocked, you'll be able to get your regular brand, but if their supplies are exhausted, don't forget that Canadian stores do not sell U. S. cigarettes or tobacco. On the average, prices will be a little higher than in the United States.

Books and Magazines: If you like to read, take along magazines or books; perhaps you can exchange with your fellow passengers, and you'll find that something to read will help pass the time—make a more pleasant trip. Card playing is permitted, but the Company will not be responsible for any losses resulting from gambling. Our advice is—don't gamble—or if you do, play for small enough stakes that you don't get hurt. The Company provides a wide selection of books for your use and enjoyment at the Whitehorse camp.

Spare Time: You are going to Alaska or Canada to do a very important war job, and you'll probably have little or no spare time. Right now, that's not so important. E. W. Elliott employees, however, are usually given every fourth Sunday off, and if you like to hike or explore new ground, here's your chance. Except for the winter months, you'll probably find the best fishing in the world, so if you're a fisherman, take your gear along. You may come back with some new fish stories.

—10—

The Employment Contract: Most of the provisions of the employment contract which you sign are covered elsewhere in this booklet, but be sure to read the agreement carefully before you sign it, and if anything is not completely clear to you, ask us to explain. This is a standard form of government contract for work of this type and you will be expected to live up to the obligations it imposes on you if you are to receive the benefits which are offered. You will be given a copy of this agreement when you are employed.

Letters from Home: The mail service is apt to be very slow both in Alaska and Canada—these are both War areas and Government communications come first, so caution your family that it will be quite a while before they hear from you. It will also be some time before you get a letter from home, too. If you are employed for work at Whitehorse or vicinity, tell your folks to send your mail to you in care of E. W. Elliott, General Contractor, Whitehorse, Y. T. There is both regular and airmail service to Alaska and Canada, but delivery is uncertain because of weather conditions and limited facilities for handling mail in these areas. Whenever possible the name of the camp where you are working should be noted in the lower left-hand corner of the envelope to expedite transmittal of your letters. Our job office there will see that your mail reaches you. Tell your families not to worry if they don't hear from you. In an emergency you can always send a wire. Personal stationery and writing materials are furnished free of charge at our job locations. Just remember that you'll be a long way from home, and while it naturally won't be easy on your wife and family, they'll accept your absence with much better grace if you write often.

Terminations: When you leave our employ the job office will furnish you with a copy of your termination notice on which will be shown the reason for your separation. This notice will probably have quite a bit to do with whether or not you will be hired for other war work in the future because your next employer will want to know whether or not you have been released by us for other work. If your work has been satisfactory, we will release you without prejudice, but in the event that you have not proven yourself to be the right kind of a man, competent workman, or if you wilfully refused to accept normal directions in your work, we are not required by law to give you this release. Without it, you may have trouble getting other war jobs.

If you have completed your employment contract or complied with all of its terms, you will be eligible for return to your point of recruitment at Company expense. This does not mean,

—11—

however, that you can go home for a short trip and return to the job again at our expense. Our policy in this regard is that if you leave the job while there is still work to be done, even though you may have completed your working agreement, you will not be considered for re-hire unless you have a written request from the job, stating that they want you back. This can be noted on your termination slip or can be in the form of a special letter, so if you are interested in being re-employed by us, you had better see you get such written evidence of our willingness to re-employ you before you leave the job.

If your services are terminated at your own request before your employment contract has been completed, you will only be considered for re-employment upon presentation of written evidence of your desirability as outlined above and in this case you will be required to pay the cost of your transportation back to the job site.

Upon your arrival at the job you will be re-hired and, in order to qualify for free transportation home, you will have to sign a new contract and work for the full period stated therein. Men returning to Whitehorse at their own expense will probably not be permitted to use the Company vessels, but must arrange their own transportation on commercial ships.

Leave of Absence: There are no provisions for "Leaves of Absence" from work except in the case of administrative and supervisory employees, so if you leave before the expiration of your contract and expect to return to the job, you must immediately notify the Seattle office of the Company so that your draft deferment will not be cancelled. If you should return to the job on your own responsibility and at your own expense without having previously made arrangements with us to continue or extend your deferment, you will have to pay your own fare home should you be called into the Army.

About the Job: This project is generally referred to as the "Alcan Highway Job," and while it has to do with building a road to Alaska, most of the work is located in Canadian territory. This company is working at a number of places and you may be hired for any one of the job locations, depending upon our needs at the time of your employment. The Company reserves the right to transfer you at any time from one job location to another.

In most cases, you'll be hired for work on the northern part of the project. In that event, you'll go to the West Coast by rail, probably to Skagway, Alaska, on Company operated ships, and

—12—

then inland by rail again to the vicinity of Whitehorse, Y. T.—from there you may be sent by truck to one of the road camps. Should you travel this route, you will find the Alaska trip by water one of the most interesting and unusual voyages in the world. You'll sail through the famous "inside passage" to Alaska, almost a thousand miles of inland waterway—protected from the open sea by hundreds of islands which form its outer edge. As a result the water is, for the greater part, as calm as an inland lake during most of the year. Winter time, of course, brings rough weather and the trip is not pleasant. In any event, you'll see a land of remarkable beauty, historic interest, and glamour—one of the world's last great frontiers.

The immediate urgent need for the Alcan Highway is to help us protect Alaska from the Japs and later, we hope, to enable us to use Alaska as a place from which to attack and defeat them. It is a very rich country with tremendous resources and we don't want to lose it. Later on the highway which you have helped to complete will be of great benefit in the development of this great land. So, you see it is important work that you will be doing, perhaps the most important, biggest job facing us today. But don't get the idea it's going to be easy going. *Weather and living conditions are plenty tough* and unless you are the kind of a man who can stand lots of punishment, you had better stay home, regardless of the high wages you might make.

In this booklet we have tried to outline the requirements of this work and tell you the things you should know in order to get to the job physically and mentally prepared to put forth your best efforts. We think you will find this company a good outfit to work for, reasonable and just in its demands, and you, in turn, are expected to treat us in the same way. *If you have questions which this booklet does not answer or if there is any doubt in your mind about what will be expected of you, we suggest that you ask us about them before you leave for the job—not after you arrive.* Thus we will understand each other and be well on our way to a pleasant mutually profitable working arrangement.

This company complies in all respects with the approved stabilization plan of the Alaska Area, War Manpower Commission. Terminations will be granted only in accordance with the terms and provisions of this plan.

E. W. ELLIOTT,
General Contractor.

—13—

QUICK ANSWERS TO FREQUENT QUESTIONS

1. Is Social Security deducted from my check?
If you are working in Canadian territory, No.
If you are working in Alaska, Yes.

2. Do I pay an Income Tax on my earnings?
As far as U. S. Income Taxes are concerned, if you are a bona fide non-resident for 12 months in the calendar year 1943, you do not have to pay an Income Tax on money you earn during this time. In other words, you may save yourself a lot of tax money by staying on the job. If you are working in Alaska, of course, you pay the tax but you do not pay Canadian Income Taxes on money earned in Canada.

3. How is the mail service?
The mail service is slow because of over-crowded transportation facilities and uncertain weather, but you can write home and receive letters from home through the mail, of course, subject to government censor.

4. What if I get sick or am injured?
The U. S. Public Health Service is charged with the welfare of all employees on the Alaska Highway job. You will be well taken care of. Your payment into the Medical Aid Fund takes care of you for other than occupational injuries or sickness.

5. Can I send money home?
Yes, you can buy drafts and send money home. The Canadian Government charges 1% Excise Tax for this service which you have to pay. It is best to send money by registered mail.

6. Can I buy clothes on the job?
Maybe, but don't count on it. Take everything you need.

7. Can I stay on after my contract is completed?
If you are a good worker and if we have more work to be done we will probably want you to stay. In this case you will not have to sign a new contract since you will already have earned free transportation home.

8. How much cash should I take with me?
You should have about $25.00 on your person when you leave home.

Steamboat Mountain, west of Fort Nelson, B.C. GA C. HAGE COLLECTION
NA-4450-33

Teslin Lake. NA 30-N-45-80

Civilians were hired from throughout the United States and Canada to replace the army troops and reconstruct the original tote road in 1943 and 1944.
AUTHOR'S COLLECTION

A PRA camp at Fort Nelson. These camps were a far cry from the army's primitive camps set up at the beginning of the project. The original camps used surplus Civilian Conservation Corps (CCC) buildings brought up from the Lower 48 or simple bell tents. Neither were adequate for the severe winter conditions in this part of North America. The PRA in contrast built more permanent structures that provided some comfort from the cold and snow.
AUTHOR'S COLLECTION

The highway ran through the broad Rancheria Valley in the Yukon. The road bisected some of the most beautiful and rugged terrain in North America. PABC

An equipment boneyard five miles east of Teslin, February 1943. NAC. FINNIE COLLECTION

Icing a corduroy section of road at Swift River, February 1943. This would provide a smoother road surface than the bumpy, small trees laid across the road for stability. NAC. FINNIE COLLECTION

Alaska's congressional delegate, Anthony Dimond (front seat) made an inspection tour of the highway in 1943. He had been an early advocate of a highway to Alaska. NA 111-SC-322952

Utah Construction Company equipment improves the grade and alignment of the pioneer road by Goose Bay, Kluane Lake. The bulldozer in the foreground is keeping the road open to traffic. The other equipment is making a cut directly across the road just ahead of the bulldozer in the foreground and at the same time is using the material to build a fill in the clearing over the culvert to the right, August 1943.

NA 30-N-43-3971

Aerial view showing reconstruction of the original pioneer road in September 1943. A multitude of tracks have been made by trucks and equipment attempting to fight their way through this swampy section. NA 30-N-43-3718

A United States Congressional committee delegation poses at a road sign in Tok, Alaska, August 1945. NA III-SC-323327

Convoys of trucks were constantly on the road delivering the supplies needed for the new road construction and for the military in Alaska whenever it was possible to get through to Fairbanks. ASL

A Canada Department of Mines and Resources truck between Fort St. John and Fort Nelson, 1943. GA C. HAGE COLLECTION

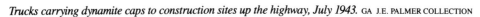

Trucks carrying dynamite caps to construction sites up the highway, July 1943. GA J.E. PALMER COLLECTION

A fire destroyed a shop at the United States Engineering Department's Whitehorse facility.
YA PRESTON COLLECTION 6162

Greyhound of Canada was contracted to provide scheduled bus service and non-scheduled shuttling of personnel once the pioneer road was finished in November 1942. Many buses throughout Canada were eventually brought to the North and some type of schedule was attempted to be maintained under the most difficult circumstances—poor weather conditions, road washouts and even conflict of commands and orders from the U.S. Army. That the company faced these hardships and maintained somewhat of a schedule for the next three wartime years, is a tribute to its persistence and drivers along the route. SPRHS

This story was excerpted from the diary of
Ernest M. Mueller of Boone, Iowa, who drove
a truck up the Alaska Highway in 1943.
It has been slightly edited.

The Alaska Highway was built in 1942-1943 by C. F. Lytle and Green Company of Des Moines, Iowa, and eighteen other contractors under the direction of the U.S. Public Roads Administration.

In 1943, Alaska is still a territory and you will need a permit to enter. The permit is registered in the Fairbanks Office and the only way out is by boat or plane. When you are ready to leave Alaska in 1943 you will need a clearance from the Fairbanks Office to buy a ticket on either the plane or boat.

A convoy of two wheel drive trucks drove over the temporary military roads in Canada, in the mud caused by the spring thaw. The road in places was covered with water and there were places that the mud could be as deep as four feet. The bridges were all temporary bridges and with the ice starting to thaw, it was risky to cross some of them. The trucks that we drove were all leftover trucks that had been used by the Public Works Administration. The trucks were in storage at the fairgrounds in St. Paul, Minnesota.

The term, temporary military road, means the long muddy hills were built with a U turn at the bottom and the U turn was filled with trees. This meant that you drove down the muddy hills and stopped at the bottom to make this U turn and then you drove up the other side in the mud. The pay scale in 1943 was $1.56 per hour for the skilled worker. Time and one half for over eight hours and double time for the seventh day of the week.

SATURDAY 3-27-43

There were four men that worked for the Lytle Green Company that left Des Moines, Iowa, at 1:15 a.m. by train and arrived in St. Paul, at eight. The Public Roads Office sent us out to the fairgrounds where 11 trucks were loaded ready to be driven to Alaska. Here at the fairgrounds we meet 18 fellows from the Peterson Construction Company. My truck is a 1937 Chevrolet short wheelbase cab over engine. It was made up to be a tool truck with a small light plant built into the box on the truck.

SUNDAY 3-28-43

It's 7 a.m. when 11 trucks loaded with tools of all kinds and 22 men start from the fairgrounds in St. Paul, Minnesota with high hopes of parking the trucks in Alaska. We stop at a small town for our Sunday dinner and the dinner was good. After eating, I take three dimes from each of the boys and try the slot machine. I make enough to pay for our dinners and buy three packs of cigarettes for each of the four fellows and have enough left for a nice tip. We are driving in rain mixed with snow most of the day. We make it to Fargo, North Dakota, by supper time and will stay here for the night.

Started from Fargo at 6 a.m. and about 10 a.m. had to cross a river that was going over its bank. The road was marked with fence posts. We stopped for lunch and bought oranges to eat. We were told not to drink the water. In the afternoon, we stopped all 11 trucks in a very small town for a break. The store was an old house with a front porch. There on the porch was this older man dressed in a blue suit with coat and vest with his chair tipped back against the house. After I bought my stuff, I came out. Under that coat of his was a big star. He said you boys are illegally parked in our town. I told him he better look at our license plates before he writes any tickets. When he saw the U.S. Government plates, he said boys you can park in our town anytime you want to. Well, we made it to Minot, North Dakota, for supper. They serviced the trucks here and we stayed here for the night.

TUESDAY 3-30-43

Started west from Minot, North Dakota, drove through the Indian reservation and made it to Glasgow, Montana. One truck had a bad generator, so we got that fixed. Had a good meal and the room and bed were fine for a good night's rest. This is flat, windy and cold country today.

THURSDAY 4-1-43

Started north from Shelby, Montana, and crossed the border into Canada. When we got into Canada we met this car that was stopped on the road. We stopped and tried to help, but the motor was stuck, so we pulled the car all the way to Lethbridge. We had dinner in Lethbridge where we are served by the first Chinese operated restaurant. The dinner is 50 cents and if you paid with a five dollar bill in U.S. money they gave you back five dollars in their money. We were escorted through the city of Calgary and there was about three inches of wet snow on the road. Tried to get rooms at Red Deer but had to drive all the way to Lacombe for a room.

FRIDAY 4-2-43

Started out early. It's only a short drive to Edmonton. Edmonton is the gateway to the North Country. Once again we service our trucks, but we did have a little time to look over part of the town. They told us to get a good night's rest so we could start out early the next morning. The frost on

Photographs of Ernest Mueller's trip on the Alaska Highway, 1943. ERNEST MUELLER COLLECTION

the road ahead might start to melt and that would be a problem.

SATURDAY 4-3-43

The road north of Edmonton is a black dirt road and by 10 a.m. the frost on the top was starting to thaw. The road got real slick. I had to stop my truck and three men had to push on the side of the truck for me to get it going forward again. We made it to Athabaska for dinner. The radio flashed the news saying the road would be closed at midnight. We drove until 11 p.m. and stopped at a filling station where we ate a sandwich and had coffee.

SUNDAY 4-4-43

At midnight, we drove across the Athabaska River on the ice and made it to High Prairie, near daylight. We had breakfast here and worked on the trucks. We started out to drive to Grande Prairie, after sundown hoping to drive on the frost. The road won't freeze again tonight.

MONDAY 4-5-43

We got stuck in the mud just after midnight and waited till daylight to get out. We didn't think to bring anything to eat or drink. The hill that we were to drive down to get to the Big Smokee River was three miles long, all ice with an S turn near the bottom. They tell us to wire the truck doors open for the drive down this hill. We crossed the Big Smokee River on the ice that was three feet thick. We just didn't understand that this kind of mud turned 16 miles into 24 hours of driving. The mud will pile up under the truck fenders till it stops the front wheels from turning.

TUESDAY 4-6-43

Drove into Grande Prairie at 10 a.m. It's a nice clean little town. The police tell us the road ahead is closed, but to check with them at midnight. The restaurant operator is Chinese and the food is very good. They serve beer down the block only on the even hours of the clock. The farmers raise wheat and tall white hogs they call a bacon hog. At midnight the police tell us the road would be all right and that we can go.

WEDNESDAY 4-7-43

The road did not freeze, but we were able to handle the mud and make it to Pouce Coupe for breakfast, only a few miles south of Dawson Creek. We made it to Dawson Creek by noon and had a nice dinner. Dawson Creek is the end of the railroad and the start of the Alcan Highway going north.

We started north in the late afternoon. Four miles of the Alcan looked pretty good, but the road was full of frost boils. We got the speed of the truck up to 40 miles per hour, but when we hit the long frost boils, we dropped into super low. We made it north to the Peace River where they are building a new bridge and it's a high one. As we crossed the Peace River by driving to the bottom of the river valley, we had to push each truck up the hill out of the valley with a dozer. By midnight, we got all of our trucks pushed to the top of the hill.

THURSDAY 4-8-43

Fort St. John is 60 miles north of Dawson Creek. It's the end of the farm country. We make our way to Mile Post 130. The camp here is called Sicking and it's a lumber camp. They let us eat supper here and gas up our trucks. We sleep in our trucks for few hours and start out again.

FRIDAY 4-9-43

We drove to Mile Post 175 where we had to leave two trucks to be repaired. One lost a rod in the motor and the other one broke a spring hanger.

We drove on to Mile Post 235 for our supper. It's here that we get a hot bath and a nice clean bed to sleep in. My foot locker was in the truck with clean clothes in it, but it was so battered up, it was impossible to open it. In the morning, I had to put on my same dirty clothes. I put the left sock on my right foot. It was so crusted that I had to change it before I could walk.

SATURDAY 4-10-43

We drove 20 miles and got to Fort Nelson for dinner. Fort Nelson is 255 miles north of Dawson Creek, but now it's Mile Post 0 going north. North of Fort Nelson about 10 miles, the trees grow so thick that you don't see any light when you look at them in the daylight. They're just as straight as a pencil. They cut them on three sides and build cabins out of them.

We started north after dinner in the mud, but only made it to the camp at Mile Post 8. The mud here is so sticky that it almost pulls your overshoes off as you try to walk in it. The mud was four to six inches deep on the big tent floor and half the fellows in the tent are sick. I got my sleep in the truck; that tent isn't for me.

SUNDAY 4-11-43

Started driving north from Mile Post 8 at midnight. They told us if we could make it 10 miles north, the road would still be frozen. Our luck ran out four miles north when it started to rain. Three of our four trucks went into the ditch on the rain-slick, mud road. They sent me back to the camp at Mile Post 8 for help and I made it back to camp late.

MONDAY 4-12-43

They got the three trucks back to camp and we worked on the trucks all day.

TUESDAY 4-13-43

Started driving north from Mile Post 8 again at 2 p.m. and this time we made it. Steamboat Mountain is about 50 miles north of Fort Nelson and the road is 14 miles up hill to get to the top. They gave it this name because the dozer made the road by going around the hills as it made its way to the top. We got to the top of Steamboat about midnight by moonlight. The road going up was pretty good, but water was seeping out of the hills and it was mud road again going down the back side.

WEDNESDAY 4-14-43

We drove until noon and found a camp where we stopped for dinner. At Mile Post 100 above Fort Nelson the Ford truck lost its clutch and that's where we left it. We are back driving 24 hours a day.

THURSDAY 4-15-43

We got stuck again after midnight and waited until daylight to get out. We drove into the woods to bypass the water holes in the road. Crossed the Liard River and the rear axle broke in my truck just two miles from the camp at Mile Post 210. The road was good enough for them to pull me into the camp at 210. I talked the Army boys out of one of their axles. Their axles are longer but the end that slips into the rear end is the same. The Army boys told me about a machine shop four miles down the Liard River on the south side. We will stay here at camp 210; the other trucks will go on.

FRIDAY 4-16-43

After breakfast, I hitched a ride with all my axle parts four miles up the road to a path through the woods to the Liard River. Crossed the river on the ice and found the machine shop. They cut off the axle and used my axle hub by welding it to the cut off axle. It was a good job but it took eight hours.

Just as my axle was being finished at the machine shop some Army boys stopped and gave me a ride back to the camp at 210. I put in my new axle, gassed up the truck, had supper and started out. About five miles up the road, the ruts grew deeper than our truck could take. We tried to drive on the top of the ruts and was doing fine until the last 50 feet when the truck slipped in. There is a light a short way up the road, some guy living in a skid-type shack with his wife and little girl. His job is to cut poles for the telephone line. With his small cat, he pulled us out of the deep ruts. We drove about three more miles and got stuck again. That's all till daylight.

SATURDAY 4-17-43

We used tree limbs to get us out of the mud hole and just got started on a dry part of the road when something gave way in the truck's rear end. I thought it was my rebuilt axle that broke again. My partner walked back to the man that was cutting telephone poles and found out there was a camp four miles further north. So that's where we walked to. We crossed a bridge which had three telephone poles cabled together to support each side. The ice had the bridge bent.

SUNDAY 4-18-43

After breakfast, I walked back to my truck to see if there was any way to get it going again. My rebuilt axle was OK, but all the rivets were sheared that held the ring gear in place. My truck, being a tool truck, had some parts bins and I found enough 7/16 bolts and nuts to bolt the ring gear back in place. Just as I was ready to go again some trucks showed up from the south. Their lead truck was one that was used in the desert sand. They called it the "Bull Elephant."

This truck had four big wheels and they all pulled; so this truck was able to go through deep mud or deep water. It pulled me through the next deep water hole. I crossed the bent bridge and had supper at 231. The ice took the bent bridge out in the night. After supper, the Army boys asked me to look at their truck. They needed it to get water from the creek where the bridge went out. They started their truck up and it ran terrible and without asking them I pulled all the wires out of the distributor cap. That was the wrong thing to do. When they got through telling me off, I put the wires back in their proper place and when they started the truck up again, we were friends again.

MONDAY 4-19-43

The Army boys had a small cat and they helped us for the next four miles. We had good roads until we got to the Coal River. Here we met the boys that helped my truck through the deep water hole south of Camp 231. The Army was taking the bridge plank off the bridge to try and free the ice around the bridge piling. The boys that were waiting to cross the bridge told the Army sergeant that they had eggs and would put a whole case of eggs next to the road if he would let us put enough plank back on the bridge so we could cross. The sergeant would be acting against his orders, but a case of eggs in the woods of Canada was like gold; so he agreed. We crossed the bridge and drove to Mile Post 260 where the Army had all the trucks tied up. We had supper with the boys that we helped to put the plank back on the bridge. This is one of their camps and we find out later that our boys have had to do their own cooking.

TUESDAY 4-20-43

We are all back together again with our old gang plus a lot more trucks the Army boys have tied up here at Mile Post 260. The snow is about eight inches deep in the woods. I am sleeping in a wrecked refrigerator truck in my sleeping bag.

WEDNESDAY 4-21-43

The Army is letting us buy things to eat at their Army P.X. The candy is real good and cigarettes are 50 cents a carton. Stayed up till midnight and listened to the wolves howl in the woods.

THURSDAY 4-22-43

The next two days were spent resting and I did some washing too. The Army boys had a picture show in the mess hall tonight. It was all about the knights of old England with no women in the picture. After the show we figured out a way to help my cold; it was getting bad. We started the light plant motor in the back of my truck and I used that heat to warm me up as I slept and got rid of a very bad cold in my chest.

SATURDAY 4-24-43

They started to let some of the trucks leave in groups of five. The road looks pretty dry. When the mud road dries, there is a real dust problem. The trucks grind the dried out mud into a powder and there is no wind in this part of Canada. The dust powder goes up in the air and settles back on the road and can get from one to three inches deep. When there was more than one truck on the road in the dust, the number two truck must follow close enough to see that lead truck at all times, or wait till the dust settles and he can see again.

EASTER SUNDAY 4-24-43

The food was good today and I am told that we will leave Mile Post 260 at 3 o'clock in the afternoon with four other trucks. I pulled up to gas the truck. The gas station is a 55 gallon barrel. The Army boy hits the barrel of gasoline twice with a fire axe and he puts the pump in the hole. Not one has caught fire yet.

The Army sent a cat to help us for the first three miles and then we were on our own. We started this all day, all night driving again, but this time we made progress. At Mile Post 294, we met the old gang and one of their trucks that was carrying gasoline in a 55 gallon barrel leaked and caught the truck on fire. When we got to Mile Post 325, a truck had broken its frame right behind the cab. We got along pretty good until 11 o'clock p.m. and there ahead as far as our lights would let us see, was water over the road. Standing by the side of the road was a dozer. The dozer was short the glass bowl under the gas tank for the starting engine. One guy held his hand under the gas tank and they got the dozer started. The road was covered with water for about a mile, but the water was only about one foot deep.

MONDAY 4-26-43

We drove all night to Mile Post 337, Lower Post, for breakfast. Both Lower Post and Fort Nelson were old fur trading stations for the Hudson Bay Company. It's here that the road changes from mud to gravel. We're only fifteen miles south of Watson Lake. We drove into Watson Lake, Mile Post 352 above Fort Nelson about 10:30 a.m. This is another control station so being early we sign in and out before we go to dinner. When you sign out they gas up your truck.

Just north of Watson Lake, there is a bad mud hole; so we stop and put on the chains. We made it through the mud and stopped again to take off the chains. As my partner throws the chain up on the truck box out goes his back. I got him back in the truck.

As we came to the next bridge, the road was even with the bridge floor, but on the other side, the road was six inches lower than the bridge floor. We were going about 40 miles per hour. The bump threw him to the top of the cab in the truck and put his back back into place. We drove to Mile Post 117 above Watson Lake. We were told the road above there was closed and they weren't able to gas up our trucks. Well they fed us a nice supper and we stayed all night for a good rest.

TUESDAY 4-27-43

After breakfast, we left Mile Post 117 all gassed up. They even packed us a lunch that we ate along the road at noon. We drove to Mile Post 57 and had a good supper and a nice clean bed to sleep in.

WEDNESDAY 4-28-43

We left Mile Post 57 and drove to Lake Teslin. Lake Teslin is 171 miles north of Watson Lake and 115 miles south of Whitehorse.

THURSDAY 4-29-43

We drove all night and pulled into Whitehorse at 10 a.m. and reported to the Public Roads Office where they told us the road further north through the swamp was not finished and we would have to go to Alaska by plane.

My partner will go on to Alaska by plane, but they need me to stay and repair some of the trucks before I go on to Alaska. I am to eat and sleep at the Dowell Construction Company and work on the trucks on the parking lot.

Alaska 1943

BY ERNEST MUELLER

The boys met our plane in Tanacross and we rode in a carry-all 152 miles to Gulkana. The road was built for one-way travel twisting around the hills. It's safer driving after dark when you can see the lights of an oncoming truck. The road goes right past Mt. Sanford, 16,000 feet high. In one place, it snowed so heavy that we had to stop and wait it out. Looking out the side of the carry-all window you couldn't see the ground. It only lasted about five minutes.

Tok Junction will be one of Alaska's big repair depots just off the Alcan Highway. From here they can make service calls 100 miles in three directions. Tok is 220 miles south of Fairbanks; 142 miles from Gulkana; and going south it's 100 miles to the big Army airport at Northway. Well, our little convoy is ready to make that trip to Tok but at one spot in the mountains, the water is running across the road like a small fast creek. The boys think my truck is the best one to test the road to see if it is still there. If I miss, it's about 500 feet down the hill to the creek below. I made it and on we go. Again we drive past Mt. Sanford.

The road up to Tok is the same winding, one-way road, but you have to say it's pretty. Our new garage has eight stalls for trucks, but they don't have the overhead doors on yet. We start by making our beds in the garage parts room and use papers to close the window openings. They have a small mess hall. The poor cooks have their problems just trying to fix a good meal. The only water that they have is untreated river water; the potatoes were frozen and are now thawed out; and they do their best to screen the bugs out of the flour. We have plenty of breakfast food with plenty of dried milk but the meat is either bacon and ham one day, and the next day it's ham and bacon. The little shacks that they have on the grounds are for washing your hands and face; they have their water supply tank on a stand on the outside. The black and brown bears are all over the place and one bear has a gallon can that had some jelly left in the bottom.

Gulkana roadhouse. ERNEST MUELLER COLLECTION

The bridges are all temporary and they are built on pilings and covered with gravel on the bridge plank to add the weight. Their problem is the rivers are mostly rock bottoms and any old tree that comes down the river can take the bridge out. The Tanana River flows between 11 and 18 miles an hour. It's a big river.

My work shift will be from midnight to twelve noon and I am to do all the welding plus make service calls with the wrecker in three different directions. One of the first service calls with the wrecker was to Tanacross and pull bridge sections out of the river. The bridge went out and they hired the Indians from Tanacross to steer the sections 10 miles down the river so we could pull them out and take them back to where they came from.

One of the construction gangs dug up an ivory mammoth tusk. The big end is about eight inches wide and it's about eight feet long. They cut off pieces about two inches long and the layers of ivory look like the layers of wood on a cut tree stump. The layers of ivory are simple to peel and each layer is a different color shade. The ivory does have a bad smell when they first peel it off but it makes beautiful belts and they make up the ivory to send home.

The snow is starting to show up on top of the mountain and each day it shows up a little further down the mountain. When it snows on the ground that means it's going home time. Now the fellows that came to Alaska in the truck convoys get a pleasure trip back home. They will fly to Whitehorse; railroad trip to Skagway; and the boat trip to Seattle with $120.00 for travel expense.

One afternoon about four o'clock they told us the truck is here and for us to load up and they will take us to the Northway airport. When we got our luggage loaded, we went to the office to get our $120.00, but the office was closed. So, with the truck loaded, we think we might be able to pick it up in Whitehorse.

After a plane ride to Whitehorse, the author drives down the highway to Dawson Creek in an Army six by six truck and then takes a train across Canada to his home base in Des Moines.

Hooks camp at Gulkana, Alaska. ERNEST MUELLER COLLECTION

13
OPENING
CEREMONIES

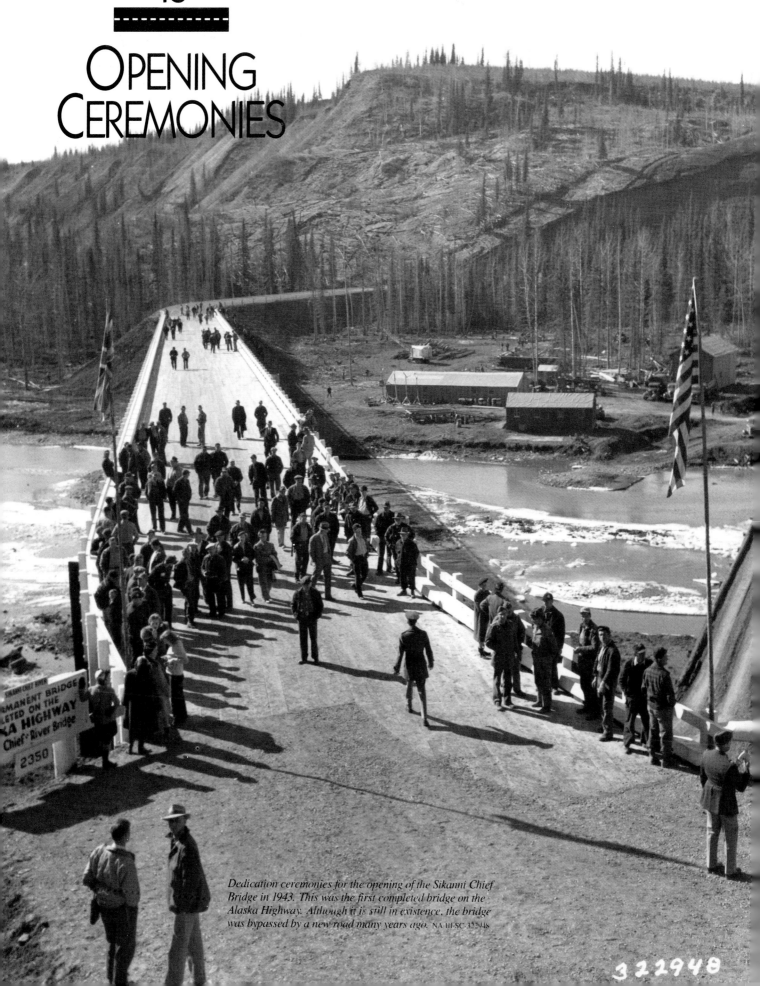

Dedication ceremonies for the opening of the Sikanni Chief Bridge in 1943. This was the first completed bridge on the Alaska Highway. Although it is still in existence, the bridge was bypassed by a new road many years ago. NA HI-SC-322948

L t. Richard L. Newberger,* an aide to Gen. James A. O'Connor, wrote this letter to Alaska Congressman Anthony J. Dimond. Dimond was unable to attend the Nov. 20, 1942 opening ceremony of the Alaska Highway at Soldier's Summit, Yukon.

The letter is chatty, informal and has some little-known details about what went on behind the scenes. It is also poetic, philosophical and contains a rare brand of humor for a military officer.

Dear Tony:

The ceremony opening the Alcan International Military Highway has come and gone and now the road is in actual operation. The first trucks have arrived in Fairbanks. Appropriately enough, the first vehicle ever driven overland from the interior of North America was piloted by a pair of enlisted soldiers, a corporal from Chicago and a private from Minneapolis. This was at the direct order of Gen. O'Connor, who felt that enlisted men should share in this culmination event of the construction of the road.

As delegate in Congress from Alaska, you will be interested in some of the background of the opening ceremony. The most interesting features of any public event always occur in that twilight zone between its evident phases and the part which is wholly preparatory. It was a ceremony international in character. Your friend Bob Bartlett led a representative delegation from Juneau. The Honorable Ian Mackenzie of the Canadian Cabinet headed an outstanding delegation from Ottawa. Gen. Geo. R. Pearkes represented Canada's armed forces. In 1914 Pearkes was a constable in the Royal Mounted at Whitehorse. He told me that some of the territory he drove over en route to the ceremony he once patrolled on horseback in a scarlet tunic. When the first World War broke out Constable Pearkes resigned from the Mounted and enlisted in the Canadian Army. He won the Victoria Cross for valor, and now commands the Pacific Command of his country.

Just as the construction of the highway demonstrated the ingenuity of our soldiers and workers on a large scale, the ceremony opening the highway demonstrated that ingenuity on a much smaller scale.

We had no printing press, yet programs seemed indispensable. What to do? Mimeographing was too colorless and drab. The blueprinting machine of the Public Roads Administration finally was pressed into service. Jean Ewen, PRA design engineer, made some excellent Arctic drawings. Gay Pinkstaff, PRA photographer, ran off the copies. The result was a program which many people thought was not only printed, but actually engraved.

It was quite a task to find distinctive food because supply

*Newberger later became a U.S. senator from Oregon.

difficulties in the wilderness are enormous as you know. We finally relied on Nature's larder. Maj. Dick Luckow sent out hunting parties. The result was moose meat, mountain sheep steaks, and a thinned-out black bear.

We gave all the groceries local names: Dawson Creek Crackers, Fairbanks Cheese, Slims River Salad which turned out to be lettuce and hot-house tomatoes. We never succeeded in convincing any of the guests that the lettuce and tomatoes were picked right outside at 40 degrees below.

Where to hold the ceremony? This problem was a stickler for a month. Finally Col. T.W. Essig made a trip over the road. He selected Soldier's Summit. This is a stretch of highway 1,500 feet above the wide swath of Kluane Lake. Above the road crags tower. Below, the lake is spread out like a vast inland sea. The setting symbolizes the vastness which the highway penetrates.

The participants in the dedication ceremony, accompanied by newspaper correspondents and photographers, drove from Whitehorse to Kluane Lake on a day that crowded 15 below. Many feet tender from the luxuries of civilization, were chilled by the time the new spruce barracks at Kluane were reached. Everyone slept that night dormitory style. The blueprinted programs were given out and privates traded autographs with colonels. A Negro soldier asked Gen. O'Connor for his autograph, and the general climbed out of his sleeping bag, put on his spectacles and signed the soldier's program. "That's the epitome of democracy, isn't it?" Bob Bartlett asked Ian Mackenzie as they watched.

When we went to bed all of us were slightly apprehensive over the fact that neither Gen. Pearkes nor Gen. Ganong of Canada's Eighth Division had arrived. They had been delayed by bad flying weather but were expected later. I think I went to sleep about 10 o'clock. Sometime later I was awakened by a gentle padding on the lumber floor. I cautiously peeked out of a corner of the bag. Gen. O'Connor, in his long underwear, with his fur cap on his head and his parka thrown over his shoulders, was tip-toeing to the door. He threw it open and a lusty "Haloo there!" came through.

The red hat bands and lapels of British general officers appeared in the darkened portal and in walked Gen. Pearkes and Ganong. I lay there in my sleeping bag and struggled between comfort and duty. The bag was warm and comfortable. Yet I was Gen. O'Connor's aide. Could I stay in bed while he welcomed our late-comers? Soon another shape in long underwear emerged. It was Col. K.B. Bush, our chief of staff. He and Gen. O'Connor, looking like union-suit advertisements, were conveying the Canadian generals to their bunks. My conscience overcame my drowsy laziness and I got up and added my size 42 underwear to the scene. "You chaps look quite nifty in there," said Lt. Bob Baile, the aid to Gen. Pearkes. This was British politeness at its kindest.

In the morning the ceremony was held. It was an event full of color, drama and significance. Col. Bush's hands became blue as he took off his gloves to read the statements received from yourself and many other distinguished men in public life. A long file of Royal Mounties stood at attention in their scarlet coats and leather boots. Their feet must have been as cold as anvils, but they stood as straight and rigid as signal poles. "Discipline and tradition account for that," said Col. Bush. Inspector William Grennan, commanding the Mounties in the Yukon, nodded his assent.

All the speakers stressed the historic importance of what was taking place . . . Ian Mackenzie spoke most eloquently for Canada and brought an inspiring message from Prime Minister King. The ceremony moved towards a natural climax. At its end Mackenzie and Bartlett were given a pair of scissors that had been specially engraved in Alaska gold by William Osborne, pioneer resident of Juneau. The crowd became tense. Then the blades closed and the red, white and blue ribbon across the road was severed. In the cold and gloom of the Arctic morning an American Army band played God Save the King, then the strains of the Star Spangled Banner filled the snowy air.

As the basalt cliffs flung back the last strains of the music a great cheer went up from the crowd. I hurried from Gen. O'Connor's side and struggled to save the ribbon for posterity. The first truck bound for Fairbanks rolled forward as the band played The Maple Leaf Forever and Washington Post.

The general had declared that rank and file soldiers, who did so much to construct the road, were to be given genuine

representation at the ceremony. The ribbon was held by four enlisted men . . . two of them Negroes, symbols of the coloured troops whose toil has played a material part in the 1,630-mile undertaking.

After the ceremony lunch was served in the barracks. The smell of spruce pitch and wood grain was still in the air. Boughs hung from the ceiling. The crimson tunics of the Mounties mingled with the somber khaki of their American allies. We ate moose meat and mountain sheep. Cigar and cigarette smoke hung beneath the beams. The band played Johann Strauss' Tales From Vienna Woods and the Blue Danube, lilting memories of a land which may soon be free. It was like some scene from a Graustrakian operetta. Inspector Grennan swayed his head to the gay waltzes, and so did the American mess sergeant who hurried along the tables seeing to it that no one's plate was empty.

It was an episode which will not soon be forgotten by those who participated in it. My own most vivid memory of it is the playing of our national anthem at Soldier's Summit. As the music faded away and I looked around me at the stern faces of the American soldiers and the grim countenances of the Mounties, I felt sure that in such as a scene as this lay the future of the United Nations — that in the ability of us all, Canadians, Americans and Alaskans, white and black, civilian and soldier, to fuse together our efforts in such a project as the Alcan Highway rests the hope of free peoples throughout the earth.

With best wishes, Tony, I am
Your friend,
Dick

The first truck from Dawson Creek, the southern terminus of the road, leads a convoy through Whitehorse 900 miles north to Fairbanks. The trip took Cpl. Otto Gronke and Pvt. Bob Bowe 72 hours to drive to Whitehorse.
YA. SIMMONS COLL. 82/192 #10

Father Charles Hamel O.M.I.
reading the invocation.
NA 30-N-43-1419

U.S. Army Guard of Honor. YA

Line up for the ribbon cutting across the newly completed Tote Road at Soldiers' Summit on Nov. 20, 1942. Representatives from the U.S. Army, RCMP, Canadian officials and Alaska officials were in attendance. The temperature dropped to −15 degrees Fahrenheit. NA 30-N-43-1420

TRUCKS ROLL NORTH ON ALASKA HIGHWAY

Ceremony in Yukon Wilderness Ends With Cutting of Ribbons to Let Them Pass

OFFICIALS LOOK TO FUTURE

General O'Connor Hails the New Bond Between Alaska, Canada and the U. S.

By THEODORE H. STRAUSS

Special to The New York Times.

KLUANE LAKE, Yukon Territory, Nov. 21 — The wilderness route to Alaska is open today, seven months and seventeen days after building of the 1,600-mile road began.

In the presence of a small group of Army officers and government officials gathered yesterday on the bleak slopes of Soldier's Summit overlooking the frozen lake below, Ian Mackenzie of the Canadian Cabinet and E. L. Bartlett, Secretary of State of Alaska, cut a red, white and blue ribbon, formally opening the Alcan International Highway.

As the first land link was completed between the United States and its great territory in the north, a thin snow swept down from the St. Elias Range, heaped in lonely grandeur to the west. Despite huge bonfires the 250 witnesses, including Grover Whalen of New York, stamped their feet to keep warm in the sub-zero temperature.

Brig. Gen. James A. O'Connor, commanding the Northwest Service Command, Mr. Mackenzie, Mr. Bartlett and others acclaimed the highway as an epic pioneering achievement significant not only as a present vital military link with the continental bastions of Alaska but also as a future pathway opening a new frontier.

Passage of First Through Truck

The exercises began at 9:30 in the morning just as a gray Arctic dawn was breaking. Colonel K. B. Bush, chief of staff of the Northwest Service Command, was master of ceremonies.

A military band played martial airs and a column of Royal Canadian Mounted Police, led by Inspector William Grennan of Dawson, commanding the Yukon force, lent color to the scene.

As the ribbon was cut, a ton-and-a-half truck, which had made the trip from Dawson Creek, the road's southern terminus, to White Horse in seventy-one hours, led a line of freight trucks past the barrier along the lonely stretch toward Fairbanks.

The first truck to make the complete run was driven by Corporal Otto Gronke of Chicago and Private Bob Bowe of Minneapolis. The muffled applause of gloved hands broke the Arctic silence as they stepped into first gear and moved northward.

Messages of congratulation were read from Vice President Wallace, Governor Ernest Gruening and Delegate Anthony J. Dimond of Alaska, Secretary of War Stimson, Lieut. Gen. Brehon Somervell, Premier William Aberhart of Alberta and Premier John Hart of British Columbia.

Mr. Wallace predicted that the road would be part of an eventual highway serving the New World from Southern South America to Siberia. Governor Gruening urged its extension to the Bering Sea and Mr. Dimond hailed it as a coordination of intelligence, energy and persevering labor.

Many speakers said that the road was a swift route to our Allies in China and Russia.

Sharing of Golden Scissors

The scissors used to cut the ribbon were gold engraved, and Colonel Bush announced that they would be broken apart, with one blade going to President Roosevelt and the other to Prime Minister Mackenzie King.

The absence most marked was that of Brig. Gen. William Hoge, who first began the building of the road from White Horse last Spring and is now on active assignment elsewhere.

General O'Connor, short and stocky, declared in response to the presentation of a service flag from the Alaskan chapter of the Daughters of the American Revolution, that the road was a bond between the United States, Canada and Alaska, and that it had a future significance which no one could now fully estimate.

He praised the all-out spirit of the soldiers and civilians who built the road. In future time, he said, men would tell their children of the building of the road, and as the tales grew taller and taller, it was possible that the Alcan Highway might become an American saga ranking with the epics of Fremont and Lewis and Clark.

Mr. Mackenzie said that Canada had provided the soil while the United States provided the toil.

Major Gen. George R. Pearkes, Chief of the Pacific Command of the Canadian Army, brought greetings from Canada's armed forces. He was accompanied by Major Gen. H. N. Ganong of the Canadian Eighth Division.

The Alcan Highway, built by United States Army engineers and a contingent of civilian workmen, must still be surfaced and its bridges rebuilt to be turned into a permanent structure. A thousand miles of it, from Dawson Creek to Fairbanks, is open and winds through a vast wilderness hardly touched by man. A new frontier has been reached.

Article from the New York Times, *November 22, 1942.*

Alaska Road Will Be Opened Friday

Army Truck Will be Vanguard of Many a Mighty Convoy

194 2

Whitehorse, Yukon Territory, Nov. 19 —(AP)— A ribbon of red, white and blue will be slashed and flung to the Arctic wind Friday, opening the Alaska highway.

Between the fluttering colors of the United States and Canada will roll an army truck manned by two proud soldiers from the ranks, to be followed by cars bearing civil and military officials or the two nations. This will be the vanguard of a series of mighty convoys—convoys safe from submarines and all but immune to air attack—which will move north toward Japan.

Dignitaries of Canada and Alaska will join the jubilant northwest service corps in celebrating the epochal engineering feat of the war, a road pushed 1,681 miles through one of the world's great wildernesses in seven months and seventeen days.

Originally planned to be only nine feet wide, it was found practicable to make the road twice that width and still maintain a construction pace of eight miles a day. Two hundred streams had to be bridged, vast areas of muskeg had to be crossed. Much of the construction was through mountains.

Hard-packed snow, kept clear by numerous snowplows, affords good winter travel. In the late spring thaw, there will be mud, and river ice crushing against bridges, to bring grave problems. But already a huge force of public roads administration workers is on the job, putting in an all-year gravel surface and building sturdy bridges.

The new road extends frim Fairbanks, Alaska, to Dawson Creek, Alberta, At its northern terminus, it connects with Alaska's sole railroad of any importance, the government line from Fairbanks to Anchorage, the army's headquarters, and with the latter city's seaports of Seward and Whittier. It also connects with the Richardson highway, which runs from interior Alaska to the seaport of Valdez.

Dawson Creek is the railhead of the Canadian National, the northern "jumping-off place" for all the vast, northwestern wilderness.

At Dawson Creek it also strikes an existing auto road to Edmonton, capital of Alberta, from which railroad and highways stretch out to a score of points on the United States border.

Paralleling the new road is a string of military airfields connecting the west and midwest with Alaska bases. Importance of supplying these vital aerial outposts was a prime reason for choosing the present route in preference to the long-favored tourist highway nearer the coast.

The American side at the ceremonies. YA

E.L. Bartlett reads a message from the governor of the Territory of Alaska. YA

Dignitaries lined up for the ribbon cutting. YA

General O'Connor addressing the crowd. YA

Program

Invocation — Father Charles Hamel, O.M.I.
Opening Remarks — Col. K.B. Bush, G.S.C.
Master of Ceremonies
Reading of Messages — Col. John W. Wheeler, C.E.
Introductions
Col. E.G. Paules - Whitehorse Sector,
Col. Robert D. Ingalls - Ft. St. John Sector;
Enlisted Men who will hold the Ribbon:
Corp. Refines Sims Jr., Pvt. Alfred Jalufka
Whitehorse Sector.
Mstr. Sgt. Andrew E. Doyle, Corp. John T. Reilly
Fort St. John Sector.
Message from the Canadian Armed Forces
Maj. Gen. George R. Pearkes.
Message from Public Roads Administration
and Civilian Contractors
Mr. J.S. Bright, District Engineer.
Message from the Premier of Alberta
by Hon. W.A. Fallow.
Further Reading of Messages — Col. Bush
Remarks — Dr. Charles Camsell
Commissioner Northwest Territories
Introduction of Insp. William Grennan, R.C.M.P.
Speech for Dominion of Canada and Reading of
Message from the Prime Minister by Hon. Ian Mackenzie
Speech for Territory of Alaska and Reading of
Message from the Governor by Hon. E.L. Bartlett.
Response on behalf of the American Army,
Brig. Gen. James A. O'Connor, commanding N.W. Serv. Command
Cutting of Ribbon — Mr. Mackenzie, Mr. Bartlett
"GOD SAVE THE KING" - "THE STAR SPANGLED BANNER"
U.S. Army Bands
Benediction Capt. Erwin T. May, Chaplain, U.S.A.

ALASKA-CANADA HIGHWAY

DEDICATION
KLUANE LAKE -YUKON-
NOVEMBER · 20 TH · 1942 ·

Menu

SUPPER
Thursday, November 19, 1942 · 6 PM

ST. ELIAS MOUNTAIN SHEEP
Mosheep Brown Gravy
Spinach à la Kloo - Takhini Corn
Tanana Potatoes
SLIMS RIVER SALAD
Chisana Apple Sauce - Siwash Geldin
Coffee à la Yukon
China-Way Tea
Moose Milk
Sour Dough Bread - Bull-Dozer Butter

⊕

BREAKFAST
Friday, November 20 · 7:15 AM

Burwash Prunes
Grapefruit Juice · Alcan · Tomato Juice
Alberta Farina
Aishihik Sausage - Dezadeash Eggs
Toast - Butter
Coffee - Sugar - Milk

DINNER
Friday, November 20, 12 Noon

CHAMPAGNE SOUP
MOOSE STEAK à la Donjek
Pickhandle Beans - Kaskawulsh Potatoes
Nabesna Peas and Carrots
KLUANE SALAD
HORSE CAMP PUDDING
Dawson Creek Crackers - Fairbanks Cheese
1630 Miles Coffee
Tea - Orange Juice - Milk
Bread - Butter

COMMITTEE: Col. T.W. Essig, Maj. R.C. Luckow,
Maj. E.N. Stans, Capt. P.L. Reed Capt. R.R. Johnson,
Lt. F.C. Bishop, Lt. B.B. Miller, Lt. R.L. Reuberger.

The RCMP Guard of Honor. YA

The honorable Ian Mackenzie reading a message on behalf of Prime Minister Mackenzie King of Canada. YA, SIMMONS COLL. 82/192 #8

Brig. Gen. James O'Connor, left, watches as E.L. "Bob" Bartlett, middle, and Ian Mackenzie cut the ribbon.
YA, SIMMONS COLL. 82/192 #9

Members of the RCMP Guard of Honor. YA

Additional views of the invocation with the RCMP Guard of Honor. U.S. ARMY & LC-USW33-932-ZC

Dedication of the Peace River Bridge on Aug. 31, 1943. ASL. ALASKA HIGHWAY COLL.. PCA 193-80

V-E Day celebration on a baseball field in Whitehorse, May 8, 1945. The highway had served well in the defense of Alaska and Northwest Canada. USA SC 323309

Pond and Kulich standing at Soldiers' Summit overlooking Kluane Lake. KEN SPOTSWOOD PHOTO

The actual site of the Nov. 20, 1942, dedication ceremonies visited by Yukon Anniversaries Commission Executive Director Ron Pond, left, with Marty Kulich and Lindsay Bourne of Stellar Productions of Vancouver, B.C., who is producing the re-dedication ceremony on Nov. 20, 1992.
KEN SPOTSWOOD PHOTO

14

THE CANOL PROJECT

Welding pipe.
NAC FINNIE COLLECTION, PA 171533

anol is an epic of the North, and of parts of the North where, in the words of Robert W. Service, "the mountains are nameless and the rivers all run God knows where." But Canol is also a war story.

Alaska was not wholly defenseless. But its bases were few and inadequate. They could be supplied only by sea or air. By land there was no through road, not even a trail, between Alaska and the most northerly extensions of existing Canadian rail lines or highways connecting with those of the United States.

To overcome this gap in our vital defenses, the United States Army in March of 1942 started building the Alaska Highway. Its southern terminus at Dawson Creek, British Columbia, it would give us an emergency land route 1,600 miles long to Fairbanks in the heart of Alaska. But, still more important, it would tie in a chain of airports and flight strips for the use of fighter planes, bombers, and transports.

The Canadian Government had already carved out airports between Edmonton, Alberta — Canada's most northerly city — and Whitehorse, Yukon Territory, nearly a thousand miles to the northwest. These linked others in Alaska, on which initial construction had been done by the U.S. Civil Aeronautics Authority. All of the airports would have to be enlarged to accommodate ever-increasing traffic — including Lend-Lease fighters and bombers being ferried to our ally the Soviet Union — and intermediate emergency strips must be built.

The trucks using the Alaska Highway would need fuel. The planes using its fields would need fuel.

And when the Alaska Highway was begun there was no certainty that the shipping lanes to Alaska could be kept open. Besides, the tankers required to fuel the highway were in urgent demand elsewhere.

But there was oil available in the North — a known and already producing source.

In the wilderness of northwestern Canada oil had been found along the banks of the Mackenzie River more than 150 years ago and had been developed on a small scale since 1920. It was at Norman Wells, the most northerly producing field in North America, seventy-five miles from the Arctic Circle.

And this oil had some important virtues. It had a paraffin base and a low pour point — it would flow at temperatures down to 70 below zero or lower. The extent of the field was unknown, but geologists estimated that with additional wells it could be counted on to produce 3,000 barrels of oil a day.

Out of this combination of circumstances the United States War Department evolved a plan. With the consent of the Canadian Government, the Corps of Engineers, United States Army, aided by civilian contractors, would develop the Nor-

man Wells field to produce at least 3,000 barrels of oil a day. Simultaneously they were to run a pipeline to a point on the Alaska Highway and there build a refinery to turn the Norman crude into gasoline for planes and trucks and other uses. This point was at the Yukon town of Whitehorse, head of navigation on the Yukon River system, with rail connection to tide water, and about midway along the highway. That was the plan.

It marked the beginning of the greatest construction job since the Panama Canal. In respect to area covered, time of accomplishment, and sheer pioneering, the pipeline and refinery project, combined with the Alaska Highway, was destined to become the biggest construction program in the history of the world.

It was named Canol-short for Canadian Oil.

THE COUNTRY

What sort of country was to be the setting for Canol? In popular fancy it was a forbidding land of snow and ice, not much else. It included hundreds of thousands of square miles extending from Edmonton northward almost to the Arctic Circle, along the great Mackenzie River, and westward to the Yukon Territory and Alaska.

Before the Canol Project and the Alaska Highway were completed, many thousands of men — and women too — would have learned about the snow and ice from personal experience; but they would have learned also of a warm summer with continuous daylight, flies and mosquitoes, mud and dust. Some would hate the country. Some would love it and plan to settle there after the war. None would ever forget it.

But until June 1942, first-hand knowledge of much of the country to be traversed or developed by Canol was confined to a few explorers, prospectors, traders, and Indians. The Yukon Territory was of course famed for the Klondike Gold Rush of '98, but the Mackenzie District had scarcely been heard of at all by the public.

Of the three provisional districts comprising Canada's Northwest Territories, Mackenzie, with a total area Of 527,490 square miles, has the greatest advantages of climate and accessibility as well as large natural resources.

Precipitation is moderate throughout the year. In summer there are three months of continuous daylight, when the thermometer rises to 70° and higher. In winter there are prolonged periods of sub-zero weather, but seldom colder than 50° below.

The Mackenzie River flows through a broad, almost level forested plain between the Cordilleran highland on the west and the more subdued but rugged, partly treeless Lauren-

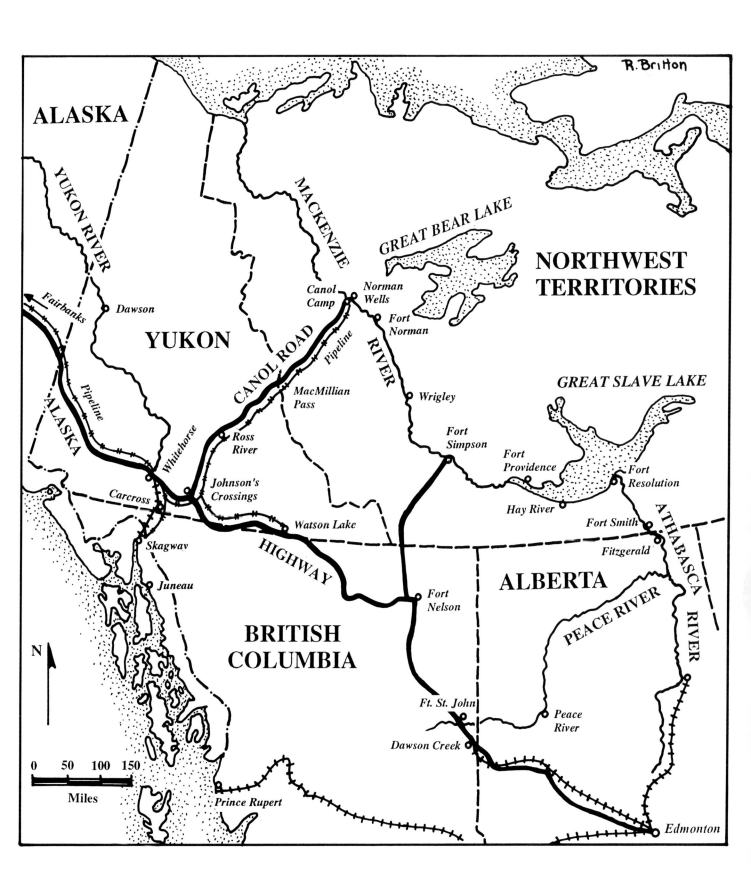

R. Britton

ALASKA

YUKON RIVER

MACKENZIE

GREAT BEAR LAKE

NORTHWEST
TERRITORIES

Fairbanks

Dawson

YUKON

Canol
Camp

Norman
Wells

Fort
Norman

GREAT SLAVE LAKE

Pipeline

CANOL ROAD

Pipeline

RIVER

MacMillian
Pass

Wrigley

ALASKA

Whitehorse

Ross
River

Fort
Simpson

Fort
Providence

Fort
Resolution

Carcross

Johnson's
Crossings

Hay River

Fort Smith

ATHABASCA

Skagway

Watson Lake

HIGHWAY

Fitzgerald

ALBERTA

Juneau

BRITISH
COLUMBIA

Fort
Nelson

PEACE RIVER

RIVER

N

Ft. St. John

Peace
River

Dawson Creek

0   50   100   150

Miles

Prince Rupert

Edmonton

The main office of Bechtel-Price-Callahan, the main CANOL contractor, on Jasper Street and 109th Street in Edmonton, November 1942. YA, FINNIE COLLECTION

tian Plateau or Canadian Shield on the east. Emptying into the Arctic Ocean, it is second in North America, in length and drainage, only to the Mississippi. It was first explored to its delta by a Scottish fur trader named Alexander Mackenzie, in 1789.

Until the nineteen-twenties transportation was exclusively by dog team in winter and by boat in summer, with paddle-wheel steamers replacing the canoes and York boats of the early days. In 1928 commercial aircraft entered the Mackenzie District. Vast areas were prospected and thousands of claims were staked. In 1931 mining of silver and radium was begun at Great Bear Lake, and the following year the oil deposits on the lower Mackenzie were drawn from to fuel the new industry. By 1938 gold was being mined at Great Slave Lake.

Mining development was expedited by tractors as well as boats and aircraft. A winter tractor road was constructed from railhead in the Peace River country 400 miles to Great Slave Lake, and the first tractor-drawn load of freight was delivered to the mining town of Yellowknife in 1939.

For nearly a century and a half before the coming of the prospectors and miners, fur traders and missionaries had lived among the northern Indian tribes. There were little settlements dotting the banks of the Mackenzie all the way to the Arctic, and at these settlements the traders and missionaries cultivated gardens in which vegetables flourished in the alluvial soil in the warmth of the unending days of summer.

The Fort Norman area of the lower Mackenzie, which was to become the focal point of the Canol Project, had first been tapped for oil in 1919-1920, but the wells were capped for lack of a market until mining development and northern aviation warranted their reopening in 1932. In 1939 an 840-barrel-per-day straight-run refinery was installed at Norman Wells,

52 miles downstream from the old trading post of Fort Norman, and from three wells there was an annual production of up to 24,000 barrels, which was sufficient for the district's requirements. The plant was operated only in summer.

Over on the other side of the divide, in the Yukon Territory gold was being recovered nowadays by dredges, while a few hundred sourdoughs panned the creeks for pay-dirt, or trapped, or traded with the Indians; and into their ramshackle villages such as Carcross, Whitehorse and Dawson came a trickle of tourists each summer to contemplate the scenes and relics of the Gold Rush. Thus it was until the spring of 1942, when the first U.S. Engineer troops sailed to Skagway, Alaska, then moved into Whitehorse to start building the middle segment of the Alaska Highway.

So that was the Yukon, and that was the Mackenzie District, until Canol began—pretty well explored in a general way and sporadically developed, but not very well understood by outsiders. One stretch of country remained that hardly anyone knew anything about, and that was where the pipeline was to be put. It was the Mackenzie-Yukon divide.

Some gold seekers crossed the divide from the east during the Klondike rush, and Indians sometimes went back and forth on hunting and trapping forays, but the only man to have walked over and written about the section lying between Fort Norman and Whitehorse was Joseph Keele of the Canadian Geological Survey.

In 1907-1908 Keele made his way from the Yukon up the Ross River, a tributary of the Pelly, reached the height of land at Christie Pass (4,525 feet), then descended the Gravel River—now called the Keele—to the Mackenzie. He heard of other routes on the Macmillan and Stewart Rivers, which are said to traverse valleys lying well below timber line, containing small lakes and an ill-defined parting at the divide. He found that "on the western slope the water flows from near the divide, for a long distance, through valleys of mature erosion with an easy grade before reaching the master stream, the Yukon; while the streams on the eastern slope fall rapidly for a comparatively short distance and reach a much lower level at their junction with the Mackenzie."

And that was just about all the information the people who were going to build the pipeline had to start with.

THE CONTRACT

The decision to construct the Canol Project was reached by the War Department at the end of April 1942, and assigned to the Corps of Engineers. The firms of W. A. Bechtel Co., H. C. Price Co., and W. E. Callahan Construction Co. were invited to consider the project. A contract for the construction of a crude oil pipeline and the design and construction of the refinery and petroleum facilities was entered into on May 4 and executed on May 20 between the War Department and Bechtel-Price-Callahan, a pro-tem partnership of the above three firms and six of their associates: Bechtel Company, J. H. Pomeroy & Co., Inc., B M P Company, Gunther and Shirley Company, R. A. Conyes, and Paul Grafe.

At the same time the Standard Oil Company of California was designated by the War Department as consultant on the design and construction of the project, and the firm of J. Gordon Turnbull and Sverdrup & Parcel was selected by the Army as architect-engineer for the project. The proprietors of the Norman Wells field, the Imperial Oil Company, were responsible for the production of oil, while the Standard Oil Company of Alaska—an affiliate of Standard of California—was to operate the pipeline and refinery when they were built.

On May 27 and 28 the advance guard of the Canol Project reached Edmonton, which was to be headquarters. There were the Officer in Charge for the Corps of Engineers, and officials of the Constructor, the Architect-Engineer, and the United States Engineer Department.

Twenty-five hundred Engineer troops with hundreds of tons of equipment were now pouring through Edmonton. They were sent over the Northern Alberta Railway 285 miles to Waterways, the end of steel and the starting point for an eleven-hundred mile water trek to Norman Wells.

At the outskirts of the little frontier town of Waterways

the troops set up a camp, and soon they were sending northward pontoon rafts loaded with foodstuffs, construction equipment, and pipe.

The route lay 285 miles down the Athabaska River, through Athabaska Lake, down the Slave River to Fort Fitzgerald, where navigation was interrupted by sixteen miles of rapids. All freight must be portaged to the foot of the rapids at Fort Smith, administrative headquarters for the Mackenzie District, then reloaded and sent on down the Slave River 190 miles to the delta, 150 miles across Great Slave Lake (fifth largest on the continent), and on down the Mackenzie River itself 500 miles to Norman Wells.

In the initial planning it had been the Army's intention to do all the hauling, to deliver all the freight—an estimated 50,000 tons—to the job site. But time was the essence, and it became apparent that all available facilities and agencies would be needed. So along with the Army worked the Constructor and the Hudson's Bay Company and the Northern Transportation Company. Both of the latter companies already had boats and barges operating on the Mackenzie River system, and the Army and the Constructor brought in diesel tugs from the Missouri and they assembled prefabricated wooden barges (later, steel ones too) at Waterways.

For construction jobs in remote lands native labor is usually available; for this one there was practically none, because the Indians were few and scattered and, while some acted as guides, dog drivers and river pilots, their usefulness as a group was negligible. Because of Canadian wartime labor restrictions based on a shortage of manpower comparatively few Canadians could be used. So the bulk of the workers had to come from the United States.

Bechtel-Price-Callahan knew that the job would be tough, and in their employment offices from Edmonton to Dallas, and from New York to San Francisco, they posted a sign:

THIS IS NO PICNIC
WORKING AND LIVING CONDITIONS ON THIS JOB ARE AS DIFFICULT AS THOSE ENCOUNTERED ON ANY CONSTRUCTION JOB EVER DONE IN THE UNITED STATES OR FOREIGN TERRITORY. MEN HIRED FOR THIS JOB WILL BE REQUIRED TO WORK AND LIVE UNDER THE MOST EXTREME CONDITIONS IMAGINABLE. TEMPERATURES WILL RANGE FROM 90 DEGREES ABOVE ZERO TO 70 DEGREES BELOW ZERO. MEN WILL HAVE TO FIGHT SWAMPS, RIVERS, ICE AND COLD. MOSQUITOES, FLIES AND GNATS WILL NOT ONLY BE ANNOYING BUT WILL CAUSE BODILY HARM. IF YOU ARE NOT PREPARED TO WORK UNDER THESE AND SIMILAR CONDITIONS DO NOT APPLY.

June 15, 1942   Bechtel-Price-Callahan

Prefabricated barges were brought by rail to Waterways and assembled there. Through the summer of 1942 they were finished and launched at a rate of two or three per day. Then they were loaded and immediately sent north. CANOL, unlike almost any other construction job, had to build its own transportation system and move a thousand miles and more not only its own equipment and machinery but foodstuffs, housing, and all the trappings of civilization for thousands of workers. Before the project could be finished, between 60,000 and 70,000 tons of freight would have to be shipped down the Mackenzie River. YA, FINNIE COLLECTION

At the foot of the rapids was Fort Smith, where the barges were launched and loaded again. Everything had to be trans-shipped, including thousands of tons of pipe. The four-inch pipe came in lengths of 20 to 22 feet, each weighing about 230 pounds. NAC

Two hundred and eighty-five miles north of Waterways, navigation in the Slave River was interrupted by 16 miles of rapids with a drop of more than 100 feet. Here, at Fort Fitzgerald, everything had to be unloaded and portaged. NAC

Troops at Waterways.
YA FINNIE COLLECTION

Climaxing their long journey the truck convoys and the tractor trains made a four-mile crossing of the frozen Mackenzie from Norman Wells to CANOL Camp. By the middle of April the spring thaw was under way; the overland road was becoming impassibly muddy and the river ice was flooded. That was the deadline. As long as the ice bridge carried water it was pretty safe, but when holes opened up and the water drained through, the ice would become candled and treacherous. But the winter road had served its purpose, and the season's freight was delivered—9,000 tons of it—without loss.
NAC FINNIE COLLECTION, PA 175986

Base camp at Peace River, the end of the railroad, 300 miles northwest of Edmonton. Between here and Norman Wells a 1,000-mile winter freighting route was opened up. YA FINNIE COLLECTION

Still they came. They came from Texas and Oklahoma, from Oregon and California, from Minnesota, Wisconsin, Kansas, Missouri and New York. There were welders, carpenters, cooks, ironworkers, cat-skinners, crane operators, truck drivers, mechanics, office workers—all hoping to play their parts in this saga of the North. And they were amazed at the distances they had to cover—even the men from Texas, who were accustomed to wide open spaces.

In another respect Canol was unlike other construction jobs. It had to create most of its own transportation facilities, and move all its supplies and equipment and housing for thousands of men a thousand miles to the job site before actual construction could be started. There were already settlements along the Mackenzie, to be sure, and there were boats and barges too, but they were hopelessly inadequate to do more than supplement the necessities that must be imported.

Military and civilian camps were erected at Waterways, Fort Fitzgerald, Fort Smith, the Slave Delta, Fort Resolution, Hay River, Wrigley Harbor, Fort Providence, Fort Simpson, Fort Wrigley, and Norman Wells. Opposite Norman Wells, four miles across the river, virgin ground was broken for Canol Camp, which was to be the starting point for the pipeline road over the mountains to Whitehorse.

Boats and barges made trip after trip down the rivers all summer long, braving the hazards of shallow water on the Athabaska, sudden storms on Great Slave Lake, and sandbars and swift water on the Mackenzie. Several loads of pipe dropped into the Slave River, and Great Slave Lake claimed a half-dozen tractors and a couple of motor graders. But considering that most of the men operating the boats and handling the freight had never before been in the North, the record was creditable.

However, try as they would, the Army and the Constructor could not get all the necessary freight to Norman Wells and Canol Camp before freeze-up. The season was just too short, with only five months of open water. Assistance was given by Canadian Pacific Airlines, whose planes carried personnel, mail and express to Norman Wells, Canol Camp and intermediate points. Bechtel-Price-Callahan augmented this commercial service with bush planes of their own.

But the ski- and float-equipped planes in northern use could carry only small pay loads and were immobilized during the long periods of freeze-up and break-up. Large transport planes were needed, and transports operated on wheels. Unfortunately there wasn't a landing field in the whole Mackenzie District. So the Constructor was asked to build a chain of airfields with the aid of the Engineer troops. That was in August. Before freeze-up ten fields had been carved out between Edmonton and Norman Wells, and an Army transport made the first landing at the Wells on the 30th of September.

But the building and maintaining of airfields and the operating of airplanes were not in the prime contract, nor were the building and operating of boats and barges and the building and operating of freight transfer camps. They came under the heading: "Supplemental Agreement." There would be more supplemental agreements before the Canol Project was finished.

Richard Finnie

Born in the Klondike, the son of the first Director of the Northwest Territories and Yukon for the Department of the Interior and grandson of the founder of the Dawson Daily News, Richard Sterling Finnie had the North in his blood.

At seventeen, he served as a radio operator under the famous Captain J.E. Bernier on board the *Arctic*. Voyages in the mid-1920s took him far north to the tiny outposts and whaling stations among the islands of the Eastern Arctic. Thanks to several fellow crew members who had expertise in photography and journalism, Finnie learned the basics of motion-picture filming and production.

He put his new skills to good use several years later, when he was appointed historian to the Canadian Government Eastern Arctic Expeditions. His first film, *In the Shadow of the Pole*, is a record of the 1928 voyage of the S.S. *Boethic*. It features the hustle and bustle of an outport at "ship time," when new provisions are unloaded at the docks. Over the next 10 years, he produced a variety of films and wrote several books on the North.

Thanks to his knowledge of the North and his filmmaking experience, the U.S. Army Engineers retained Finnie's services in 1942 to document the construction of the Alaska highway and pipeline. As part of this massive project, Finnie produced some 45 reels of film and thousands of still photographs. Its success resulted in an invitation from the international engineering giant Bechtel to serve as company historian and film producer. Over the next quarter century, Finnie produced more than 60 films documenting projects in all corners of the globe. He often served as his own cameraman, writer, director, soundman and narrator.

Richard Sterling Finnie died in 1987. His collection of films, photographs, manuscripts and sound recordings was donated to the National Archives of Canada by his wife. It contains some of the most impressive film footage ever taken of life in Canada's North.

Reprinted from the Klondike Sun, *Dawson City, Yukon.*

Prince Rupert, B.C., became an important trans-shipping point for CANOL project equipment because of its rail link with interior British Columbia and Alberta.
YA FINNIE COLLECTION

The Skagway wharf was upgraded to handle the increased flow of supplies for both the highway and CANOL projects.
YA FINNIE COLLECTION

Pipe was transported by train from Skagway to Whitehorse where it was off-loaded and trucked to the CANOL road beginning at Johnson's Crossing. YA FINNIE COLLECTION

Army troops being entertained outdoors at Fort Smith, NWT, in 1942. GA

Barges were used to transport machinery and supplies down the Mackenzie River. NAC FINNIE COLLECTION

Army troops gather in a store at Fort Resolution, NWT, in 1942. GA

THE SUPPLEMENTS

The prime contract had seemed relatively simple – albeit great in scope – to build a refinery and a pipeline and necessary access roads. But the location complicated it, for the building had to be done in partly unexplored wilderness a thousand miles from the nearest sizable city. Then, to ensure economic distribution of the petroleum products, additional pipelines and facilities must be provided. And there was the Japanese situation in the North Pacific.

All of these factors caused Canol to grow. The Army and the Constructor were obliged to carry out supplement after supplement to the prime contract.

The first was for the building of the Skagway-Whitehorse pipeline, and moving freight through Prince Rupert.

When Canol began, Alaska was in immediate danger of attack; and in June there were [Japanese] in the Aleutians. The U.S. Army and Navy were pouring men and materiel into this theater. Mainland and island defenses were strengthened at top speed. The Alaska Highway was being pushed toward Whitehorse and Fairbanks.

In that frenzied period the building of Canol took second place, and there was no room for its supplies in Pacific Coast ports or on Alaska-bound ships. The pipeline would have to be started from one end only, from Norman Wells, far removed from any likely scene of conflict.

Then circumstances changed.

The [Japanese] on Attu, Agattu and Kiska were pinned down by our bombers and harassed by our fleet until they were unable to move closer, and their submarines were driven from our shores.

Studies indicated that the pipeline should be built from both ends, and that until it and the refinery were in operation – which would take a year or longer – a supplementary line could profitably be installed between Skagway and Whitehorse to feed imported gasoline to the Alaska Highway and its airfields, thus relieving some of the strain on the railroad. The Inside Passage to Skagway became available for Canol as well as Alaska Highway shipping after the [Japanese] in the Aleutians had been brought under control; and once the Alaska Highway was passable as far as Whitehorse, it, too, could be used for Canol freighting.

With an assured gasoline supply at Whitehorse in the immediate future, a distribution system must be created along the Highway to the various airfields. Gasoline would be piped from Whitehorse nearly 900 miles between Watson Lake and Fairbanks. That, too, called for supplemental agreements.

There were still others. A thousand-mile winter road down the Mackenzie Valley must be built and used, additional boats and barges must be provided for next season's freighting, offices and barracks and warehouses and staging facilities must be built in Edmonton as well as in the North. Although work on the prime contract went on unremittingly, its difficulties were so great that its fulfillment was delayed until all of the diverse supplements – including nearly a thousand miles of pipelines – were completed and in operation.

Fulfilment of the prime contract was dependent on transportation more than on the vagaries of sub-Arctic terrain and climate. Almost every conceivable means of transportation had to be used, by land, by water and by air. Starting at Edmonton, Canol's supply routes by land and water aggregated 9,000 miles without overlapping, and some of these had to be either created or augmented before the main pipeline could be finished.

In fact, to achieve their goal – which was to lay pipe and put up a refinery – Canol's Army Engineers and Bechtel-Price-Callahan actually pioneered more miles of road and carved out more airfields than did the builders of the Alaska Highway.

Oil rig on Goose Island in the Mackenzie River between Norman Wells and CANOL Camp, February 1944.
YA FINNIE COLLECTION

The refinery at Norman Wells, NWT, was built in 1939 to produce petroleum products for the area from the 21 producing wells in the adjacent oilfield.
AUTHOR'S COLLECTION

Tank farm at Norman Wells, 1943. AUTHOR'S COLLECTION

Tractor-trailer trains, pulled by bulldozers hauled supplies over the Mackenzie Winter Road to Camp CANOL from the railhead at Peace River.
NAC FINNIE COLLECTION

A trailer train convoy along the CANOL road in the Yukon. This turned out to be the most practical way of transporting housing and construction units along the pipeline route.
YA FINNIE COLLECTION

The CANOL road passed through Dodo Canyon on its long route from Johnson's Crossing to CANOL Camp.
YA MARY MOHR COLLECTION #24

BPC carpentry shop in Edmonton at 105th Street and 81st Avenue, November 1942. Line camp cabooses are shown being constructed.
YA FINNIE COLLECTION

Milepost at Carcajon River, January 1944. YA FINNIE COLLECTION

Until the main crude line from Norman Wells could be finished, as well as afterward, the fueling of the Alaska Highway and its airfields had to be expedited. A gasoline line tapping the Skagway-Whitehorse line was laid from Carcross to Watson Lake. The Watson Lake pipe joints were stockpiled at Dawson Creek railhead and loaded onto dollies. YA FINNIE COLLECTION

Temporary camps had to be built in many areas for the pipeline construction project and the thousands of men involved. YA FINNIE COLLECTION

A four-inch pipeline was placed along the White Pass & Yukon Route to supply gasoline from Skagway to Whitehorse and points north and south.
YA FINNIE COLLECTION

The six-inch main CANOL pipeline snaked over hundreds of miles of rugged terrain to Norman Wells.
NAC FINNIE
COLLECTION, PA 174542

The pipeliners kept plugging along behind the road builders. Though the generators were housed on sleds, the welding itself was done without protection from the weather. Welds were made—and they held—at 40 degrees and 50 degrees below zero. The pipe was laid right on the surface, which simplified construction and maintenance, whereas if it were buried it would be subjected to stress and strain in the frost-locked ground. It was placed far enough off the road to be safe from traffic, and there was little else that might damage it. In winter, moreover, an insulating blanket of snow over much of the line would keep the oil warmer than the air during periods of extreme cold; but delivery would continue even if the snow drifted away, for the Norman Wells crude would flow at the lowest temperatures ever recorded in northern Canada. YA FINNIE COLLECTION

By January 1943 gasoline was being pumped from Skagway to the Whitehorse tank farm, and it fueled the trucks that were moving supplies over the Alaska Highway. Aviation gasoline soon came in, too. Even though the CANOL Project was still far from completion its facilities were already being put to work. YA FINNIE COLLECTION

Airplanes operating in the Northwest Territories had always been equipped with pontoons in the summer, when their landing fields were the countless lakes and rivers. NAC FINNIE COLLECTION, PA 175952

Black troops were brought up from the South and placed on construction projects on both the Alaska Highway and CANOL pipeline. Although this was a new experience for the troops they tackled their jobs with determination under very adverse conditions. NAC FINNIE COLLECTION, PA 175984

THE ACHIEVEMENT

On February 16, 1944, the Golden Weld in the main pipeline was made, and exactly two months later crude oil from Norman Wells flowed into Whitehorse, where the already completed refinery began digesting it.

Then the refined products flowed out to fuel the vehicles using the Alaska Highway; they were pumped to airports and flight strips spotted from Watson Lake to Fairbanks; and they were sent down to tide water at Skagway.

During the war Canol will have played an important role in strengthening Alaska's position and speeding planes on their long journey across the North Pacific.

In peacetime the 1,600 miles of pipelines, the roads, the refinery, and the tank farms, all of which are the Canol Project, will be remembered chiefly as a means of developing new and important petroleum resources, and as the instrument which pried open a vast and rich hinterland for the joint benefit of Canada and the United States.

Thousands of men and women, both civilian and military, worked on the Canol Project. Many of them went into the Far North, lived there for periods of up to two years, and came back to tell their families and friends about it. Some of them may have emphasized the hardships, real or imaginary, that they had to bear; but their collective testimony, along with that of the thousands of people who worked on the Alaska Highway, will have forever shattered the myth of an eternally frigid, barren and inhospitable North.

Records showed, too, that the North is not necessarily dangerous to life and limb. No persons on the Canol Project were mauled by wild animals, lost in blizzards, or badly frostbitten, although many were pestered by mosquitoes and black flies. There was little illness, for no climate is more healthful than that of the sub-Arctic. There were no injuries or fatalities due to any hazards peculiar to the country, and the Army's and the Constructor's safety program was so effective that industrial casualties were few.

The Canol Project demonstrated that modern machinery and equipment can, with ingenuity and experience, be worked as successfully in the Far North as elsewhere; that good roads, telephone lines, airports, pipelines and refineries can be built there, and towns, too, where people may live in comfort and happiness.

The Canol Project was also a demonstration of cooperation between individuals, groups, and countries, without which success would have been impossible. There had to be cooperation between the Constructor and the Architect-Engineer, and between them and the other prime contractors; and there had to be cooperation between all of these civilian groups and the Army. The Army, in turn, was represented on the Canol Project not only by the Corps of Engineers but also by the Medical Corps, the Signal Corps, and the Air Transport Command; and between these groups there had to be cooperation. Lastly, there had to be cooperation between the Canadian Government and the United States Government, and between the rank and file of Canadians and the Americans who came to live and work among them in Canada. It was teamwork that carried the Canol Protect through to completion. That teamwork led to enduring friendships among all concerned, and it brought the United States and Canada still closer together.

Excerpted from CANOL: The sub-Arctic Pipeline and Refinery Project constructed by Bechtel-Price-Callahan for the Corps of Engineers United States Army 1942-1944. Text by Richard Finnie. Book produced for Bechtel-Price-Callahan, San Francisco, Calif., 1945.

Building the CANOL road was as difficult, if not more so, than construction of portions of the Alaska Highway. Mud was a constant nemesis of both projects.
NAC FINNIE COLLECTION, PA 171417

*Officers from the United States
and Canadian armies inspect
the pipeline welding process.*
NAC FINNIE COLLECTION, PA 174543

*To save time, the pipeliners
often lunched on the job
instead of going back to camp,
and they thought of the sign in
the employment offices: "This
is no picnic. . . ."* NAC

*On the Feb. 16, 1944, truck
drivers and cat-skinners began
to gather at Macmillan Pass
shortly before noon. They
were here to see the tie-in of
their pipeline. There was no
ceremony. This looked just like
any other weld. But the men
watching realized the significance of the occasion. They
knew what lay behind it and
they called it the Golden Weld.*
NAC FINNIE COLLECTION, PA 172825

The world's longest continuous telephone line was constructed along with the pipeline and highway projects. The line stretched all the way from Fairbanks to Dawson Creek and from Norman Wells to the Alaska Highway. Connections were made from Dawson Creek to points east and south in Canada and the United States. NAC

Telephone linemen at work along the Alaska Highway between Tanacross and Cathedral Rapids, Alaska, October 1943. The four-inch fuel pipeline is shown. This pipe, which was never buried except at road crossings, extended from Whitehorse north to Fairbanks and south to Watson Lake, Yukon, along the highway. An additional fuel line extended north from Skagway to Whitehorse to supply the east-west line.
YA FINNIE COLLECTION

Telephone line near Norman Wells. AUTHOR'S COLLECTION

Camp
Canol
Scenes

Camp of Miller Construction Company, a subcontractor of the CANOL and Alaska Highway projects, building the telephone lines. This is at Johnson's Crossing, Yukon, the starting point for the CANOL road north.
AUTHOR'S COLLECTION

Igloos

Administration Bldg.

Barracks at Canol

A homemade snowmobile, perhaps one of the earliest built. It was powered by a motor and propeller at its rear.

Pay Day

The CANOL oil refinery tank farm. USA SC 231562

The Whitehorse refinery under construction in October 1943. The caustic treating building with the alkylation unit is being built, along with the piping trench in the foreground. YA FINNIE COLLECTION

Construction of the Whitehorse refinery was concurrent with the construction of the pipeline bringing oil from Norman Wells. YA KAMLOOPS MUS. COLLECTION

Dedication of the refinery at Whitehorse, April 30, 1944. LYMAN WOODMAN

This equipment is located near Johnson's Crossing, Yukon. Trucks and other equipment were gathered up years ago all along the old CANOL road and brought to this dump.

15

POST-WAR ERA

CEREMONY AT

WHITEHORSE

APRIL 3rd

1946

The Hand-over of Defence Projects in Northwest Canada.

————

2.30 P. M. Bands start playing.

2.45 P. M. Guard marches on.

2.50 P. M. Commanders of the Armed Forces in the Northwest.

3.00 P. M. Members of the Joint Board of Defence and other Guests.

                "The Star Spangled Banner."

                Inspection of the Guard—"The Missouri Waltz."

                   "Cock o' the North".

                General Hoge.

                The Hon. Ray Atherton.

                Symbolic Hand-over of the Projects

                    The Air Installations

                    The Land Line

                    The Highway.

                "Auld Lang Syne"

                "O Canada"

                General McNaughton

                "Road to the Isles"

                "God Save the King"

                The Guard marches off.   "Old Comrades".

HAIL and FAREWELL

Whitehorse Celebrates Another Red Letter Day in Annals of the Yukon Territory at an Impressive Ceremony Marking Transference of U. S. Projects to People of Canada.

One of the most colourful and impressive ceremonies ever to take place in the Yukon Territory was held in Whitehorse Wednesday when the official transference took place of the U. S. Army defence projects to the Canadian people. The ceremony was unique in that it culminated an international agreement mutually agreed upon between the United States and Canadian governments, undertaken in a time of stress and carried out with the greatest cordiality and mutual understanding on the part of both. At the same time it again demonstrated to the world at large the happy conditions which have always existed between the peoples of our two countries and the immense and abiding advantages accruing from international co-operation and goodwill of which we of Canada and the United States of America can well be proud. Would that other countries of the world could proclaim the existence of similar conditions between themselves and other nationalities.

This week's ceremony took place two miles out of town on the site where the first United States army made camp. Old Sol added warmth and colour to the occasion but the wind was somewhat chilly. But that fact did not deter between 2500 and 3000 people gathering to witness the unique ceremony. The raised platform was gaily bedecked with flags bunting and spruce boughs, radio network equipment was installed in its proper place and the national flags of both countries arranged so as to be hoisted at the proper time. All around snow-covered mountains and the rugged scenery so characteristic of the north formed a fitting background for the occasion whilst the buzz of planes arriving at and departing from the local airport was an added attraction which seemed to fit into the theme of the picture to a nicety.

For half an hour before the ceremony C. M. P. and United States M P.'s went into formation and marched to their allotted stations. Upon the arrival of the official party the band played "The Star Spangled Banner" and the two national flags unfurled followed by an inspection of the Guard of Honour.

The master of ceremonies was Mr. L. H. Phinney, Special Commissioner for Defence Projects of Northwest Canada. Other distinguished guests on the platform included General A. G. L. McNaughton, chairman of the Permanent Joint Defence Board; Major General G. V. Henry, also a member of the board; Major General W. N. Hoge; Brig.-General D. V. McGaffney; Brig. General G. Walsh, Hon. Ray Atherton, United States Ambassador to Canada; Major General F. F. Worthington; W C A M. Cameron of the Secretariat of the Privy Council in Canada; Admiral Schuirman and Col. C. H. Deerwester, A|V M. W. A. Curtis and Cmdr. H. G. deWolf, all members of the Joint Defence Board; Capt. Geo. Black, K. C., member of parliament for the Yukon Territory and ranking officers of the American and Canadian Armed Forces.

The Hon. Ray Atherton, in the name and on behalf of the United States government, officially made the transfer of the projects in a most appropriate address and General McNaughton accepted same in the name of the Canadian government. Other addresses included those by Brig-General McGaffney and Major General W. N. Hoge who was given quite an ovation as the one who initiated the construction of the highway and was held in the highest regard by many of his Whitehorse friends who knew him personally during his residence here. His tribute to all those who bore the brunt and burden of the day during the construction period was most appropriate and very much appreciated by his audience.

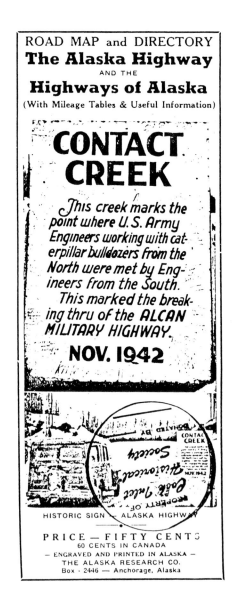
-238-

Dawson Creek, B.C.

Mile marker at the Fort Nelson Heritage Museum, Fort Nelson, B.C. EARL BROWN

Mile marker at MacBride Museum, Whitehorse, Yukon. WAYNE TOWRISS

Quonset hut remains along the CANOL road at Mile 75. GREAT BEAR GALLERY, NORMAN WELLS, NWT

One of the few structures left from the wartime construction days is this primitive tower at an abandoned airfield near Pink Mountain, B.C.

A 1936 D-8 Cat and other original construction equipment are on display at the Fort Nelson Heritage Museum, Fort Nelson, B.C.
DALE JENKINS & EARL BROWN

Tractor on display at the Watson Lake Highway Interpretive Center.

GERTRUDE

ED KERRY AND "GERTRUDE", HIS 1938 INTERNATIONAL TD 35 TRACTOR, CAME TO THE YUKON AS A TEAM IN THE 1940'S DURING THE BUILDING OF THE ALASKA HIGHWAY. GERTRUDE'S ACCOMPLISHMENTS SPANNED 40 YEARS, AND INCLUDE CONSTRUCTION OF AIRSTRIPS, CITY STREETS IN WHITEHORSE, PORTIONS OF THE ALASKA HIGHWAY, AND CONSTRUCTION SITES ALL OVER THE YUKON. "GERTIE" WAS DONATED TO THE YUKON GOVERNMENT BY THE KERRY FAMILY IN MEMORY OF ED KERRY, A LOYAL AND TRUE YUKONER.

Remains of the old trading post of Silver City, Yukon, at Mile 1020 (1693 km) near the south end of Kluane Lake. The post was on the wagon road from Whitehorse to the placer goldfields of Kluane Lake built in the early 1900s. This road was utilized by the construction workers punching the road northwest to the Alaska border. The site is now 3.1 miles/5 km off the present highway.

Some oil storage tanks built during the war are still standing at the north end of Skagway.

Remains of an oil pumping station can still be seen just north of the White Pass Summit on the White Pass & Yukon Route.

BRIDGES

Teslin River bridge at Johnson's Crossing is the third longest water span on the highway at 1,770 feet/539 meters. It was built with a high clearance to permit river steamers to pass under it. River steamers ceased operation on the river in 1942.

Monument to the memory of 1st Lt. Roland R. Small of the 18th Engineers who died near this spot on Aug. 9, 1942. He had traveled alone in a jeep for a routine check-up near his company's Kluane River camp. He apparently died of a broken back after his jeep overturned along an abandoned section of the road above a freshly cut lateral dugway. The site is 12 miles below the Donjeck River crossing in the Yukon, Mile 1083/1795 km.

Canyon Creek bridge at Mile 965/1603 km. The original bridge was built about 1920 to move freight and passengers across the Aishihik River to Silver City on Kluane Lake, and from there by boat to Burwash Landing. The bridge was reconstructed in 1942 and again in 1987.

The site of the opening ceremonies at Soldier's Summit on the shores of Kluane Lake can be seen from the present highway. A Yukon government information center is located here now.

The highway now crosses over a modern bridge at Contact Creek at Mile 573/956 km.

Canada
DEPT. OF PUBLIC WORKS
CONTACT CREEK K/M **945.2**
THIS MARKS THE LOCATION
WHERE THE CORPS OF EN-
GINEERS, U.S. ARMY WORK-
ING FROM THE NORTH MET
THOSE WORKING FROM THE
SOUTH AND OFFICIALLY
OPENED THE ALASKA HIGH-
WAY, IN OCTOBER 1942. IN
1957, CANADIAN ARMY EN-
GINEERS REPLACED THE
ORIGINAL TIMBER BRIDGE
WITH THE PRESENT STRUC-
TURE.

Watson Lake, Yukon. Over 14,000 signs are now posted at this famous site along the highway.

Remains of a construction camp, just west of Watson Lake, can still be seen.

The hot springs at Liard River, used by the troops and civilians during the construction period, is now the Liard River Hotsprings Provincial Park at Mile 477/1010 km in northern British Columbia.

Remnants of the original highway right-of-way can still be found. This section is near Watson Lake, Yukon.

Displays at the Yukon government visitor information center at Beaver Creek, Yukon.

N.A.R. (Northern Alberta Railway) complex in Dawson Creek, B.C., contains a visitor information center, museum and art gallery. It is the original station standing at the time of the highway construction.

Alaska Highway Interpretive Center in Watson Lake, Yukon, is the major center along the highway for interpretation of construction history. The famous sign forest surrounds the center.

This Dodge, ½-ton, 4×4 ambulance, manufactured in 1942, is on display at the Yukon Transportation Museum in Whitehorse. It was used by the U.S. Army on the highway construction.

This 1½-ton, 4×4 Chevrolet, G-4100/G-7100 series truck has been restored by Rudy Marek of Banks, Oregon. Hundreds of these trucks were used during the construction period. This truck will be on display on the highway during the 1992 summer 50th anniversary celebration.

This letter was written by Mike Bevan in late 1942 to his brother Tony.
Mike was a student at the University of Alberta, a member of the Canadian Army, and had some
surveying experience. He gives an interesting description of the
new highway and a Canadian's perspective of it. The letter has been edited slightly.

Dear Tony:

You rather put me on the spot, so here goes.

As you approach the Garneau Highlevel bridge to go across to the northside of Edmonton you see a sign "This is the beginning of the Alaska Highway." To be exact, it isn't, but in more than one way it is true. Over this huge bridge has gone much of the tremendous amount of road building materials which built the great 1,681 mile highway. Edmonton has been the nerve centre of this highway, from it came the men and material and the orders to accomplish what was done.

But the real highway begins at Dawson Creek and runs to Fairbanks Alaska, a distance of 1,681 miles. Not all of this highway was built by the Americans. The stretch between Dawson Creek and Fort St. John was built by Canadian contractors at the expense of the Canadian Government. It is 69 miles long. Also, along the highway the Dominion Government has built long stretches out to each settlement which was along the way. The American highway then missed these towns, much in the same manner as the Calgary-Edmonton highway bypassed many small towns, but each town has its own connecting roads. However, in the northern highway, the connecting highways to each settlement are of the same standard as the American road.

The reason the main road bypassed each settlement is due to the fact that for the last four years the Canadian government has been making airports at each settlement and it was thought inadvisable to concentrate the only two links to Alaska, the airport and the road, in the same areas, for this would make them vulnerable to bombing.

This precaution was well paid, for it was reported a Jap reconnaissance plane went over the area near Watson Lake. Undoubtedly if both airports and road had been together, they might have suffered a bombing, for Watson Lake was the closest area of the road to Jap bases on the Aleutians, an easy bombing run of about 750 miles.

The road from St. John to Dawson cuts across country. It was wide – 30 feet, and was set in a hundred-foot clearance. Nowhere did it run thru difficult terrain except where it went across the Peace River. Those of you who have never seen the Peace River cannot imagine its size. A persons imagination is limited by his experiences and until one has seen the colossal, the unbelievable, it is hard to ever picture anything else. Even up close as the Peace is to the mountains, it is still ten times wider than the Bow and very deep. On each side of it precipitous banks rise about 90′ then there is a plateau about ½-1 mile wide and another rise of about 50′.

At present the old road switchbacks down each side taking over ten miles to go 4. The new highway cuts right thru the upper 50′ wall sloping out on the plain. They are going to build a huge bridge across the Peace here. This bridge will be high above the river on massive concrete and steel pillars. It will carry the super highway from plateau to plateau. At present the only way across the Peace is by barges. These barges are pushed by sternwheelers and diesel ships. One ride on these is quite an experience.

It must be remembered that neither Dawson Creek nor Ft. St. John are as impassable places as might be imagined from reading the newspapers. On the contrary, the country is flat and inclined to be rolling. It is not as supposed, a railroad running into a mountain wall and then has to quit. The railroad stopped because of the Peace River. Around Fort St. John the country is gently rolling. Hedges help form the boundary between properties. In the fields are many fat cattle, Aberdeen Angus, horses, sheep and swine. Large crops denote the success of the farmers. Going out in the summer in an aeroplane, it was possible to see the difficulties which the engineers had to encounter.

All during the fall of 1941 they had flown over the areas, getting a lineup on the more feasible routes. During the winter of 1941-42 (especially in '42) they worked over the areas on foot, and thus got a good lead for their stadia line. With the stadia or centre line semi-laid out, it was possible then for the great speeds to be made in the actual making of the total road.

In reality, there are three roads between Fort St. John and Fort Nelson. There is the road that was not a road at all, it wound around trees, over muskeg, up and down valleys, always taking the easiest path which was the longest. It was over this road that supplies were taken up before the memorable break-up last spring. Pilots would tell you that there were so many trucks on the road that there was a path of light between Fort St. John and Fort Nelson, a distance of 300 miles. The pioneer road went on to Watson Lake a distance of 330 miles. Here the road ended. Other supplies were shipped both ways from Whitehorse, northern H.Q. of the road in the Yukon. This was a lot simpler matter, for Whitehorse is on a railroad from the Pacific Coast.

The pioneer road is not used now. The army "tote" road cuts cross ridges and fills ravines instead of going around them. However, the army tote road is nothing to brag about either. From Fort St. John the road swings out to the north carrying it farther from the mountains by the time it hits the Fort Nelson area. The general procedure was when they came to a muskeg was to dig it out and replace it with solid earth and rock. In many cases they built a corduroy road across the large muskegs (3 miles wide) and brought in earth to cover the tree trunks. This road was effective during the summer but is not efficient in spring. The tote road is not a good piece of engineering, all that was done was that they followed the pony trail between the various settlements – winding, ever winding.

As it is, too much criticism cannot be laid against this road, for they had but one instruction – to get through before winter.

To get thru, the road was organized into 4 camps. The 95th battalion Eng. was a Negro corps, working out of Fort St. John to Nelson. The 648 Eng's out of Nelson to Watson Lake. This was by far the toughest strip going over 3 ranges. Another Eng. Corp worked from Whitehorse to Watson Lake and still another from Whitehorse to Fairbanks.

The usual procedure of making road is for a transit & rod party out in front staking what is called Stadia line.

The procedure the Americans took was to sight a line between two prominent points and then direct axemen to clear a 2′ path along it, the axemen were kept on line by hand signals. Of course, sighting between various high points & especially in thick forests meant your road is going to do a lot of twisting and this it did.

Behind them would come "head cats." These machines are the largest caterpillars made, 8 cylinders and are about 10′ high. They have bulldozers in front of them and with them smash the largest trees down. It was possible for them to buck their way thru the biggest and thickest trees. First they would ram the trees thus knocking them over slightly then they lowered the bulldozer blade and lifted the trees over. They would push the trees from the centre of the road until they had make at least a 50′ clearance. These cats could dig away rock equally as well. Over the cats was a protective steel girder and a steel roof, but still some trees would topple back killing its driver and
crushing the girder. Many men were killed from falling trees, a lot more from falling over cliffs or getting drowned.

Behind the cats came smaller bulldozers who would knock off the humps and take out the smaller trees. This then left a way reasonably clear for R.D.7 and 6's or even D8's to come along with 7 or 14 yd. Le Tourneau equipment. This equipment was hydraulic, worked under oil pressure and by controls the operator was able to cut within a fraction of an inch. They would cut away the earth in a hill and fill a lot of the hollows. Working with them were bridge and culvert building crews, an important part of any road building.

Behind the large cats came small cats or C4's, that is caterpillar 4 cylinder. They'd have a small bucket on the back that would only carry 3 or 4 cubic yards of earth. They would cut out the ditches and trim the edges. Behind them came the graders who would put the finish on the road. To keep the road in shape, huge Gallion maintainers were constantly running up and down the road filling in soft spots and banking corners. This is what the road was like when it was finished.

When the Army decided to use the tote road as its standard road in places, it simply widened it, cut out many bends and gravelled it.

The present tote road leaves Fort St. John and goes NNW until it hits the Sikanni Chief. Then it goes straight north to Fort Nelson. It crosses the Sikanni at mile 117. Here many lives have been lost as the narrow road switch backs down sandstone cliffs. One large truck with a trailer went over killing 3 and injuring 11 men. At 119 there is a fair sized town where the quartermasters keep their supplies. The road runs along the top of the ridge which is above the Sikanni and seems to go up and down unnecessarily. At about mile 120 you are on the opposite side of a valley from the Rockies. It is 273 miles by the tote road to Fort Nelson. At Nelson the Sikanni joins the Muskwa forming the Nelson River. This river is as large as the Peace.

Three miles north of Nelson is the large airport at Muskwa. Although the Canadians have been building it for 3 years, it is farther behind and ½ the size of the airport the Americans built at Fort St. John in 5 months. Although the runway was 8,000′, many P-40's & P-38's piled up on its end because it was too short for their high landing speed. An interesting feature was the large Douglas Cargo planes which brought large trucks and caterpillars up north inside them. From Fort Nelson the road goes slightly WSW to Watson Lake but generally west. 50 miles out it runs into the Steamboat range. This is because of their appearance, like a steamboat prow. This escarpment was across the entire country and the road rose from an elevation of 1300′ to 4000′ in a few miles. These mountains were entirely conglomerate, made of quartz and small pebbles. They were all flat topped and ran parallel to the rockies about 15 miles away. Their structure suggested they were the shores of the Cordilleran & mountain seas which existed in that area prior to the formation of the Rockies.

The Rockies are quite high here and many have perpetual glaciers. Interesting further was the structure of the mountains great synclines and anticlines (folds in the rocks) being visible for many miles.

At 101 miles out of Fort Nelson was Summit Lake. This was a moraine lake about 2½ miles long. It was very beautiful and clear. At its lower end was a large Quartermaster Corp camp, and the lake was used as a seaplane base. From it flowed the Tetsoh river which flowed SE to join the Muskwa river about 50 miles west of Fort Nelson. From the other end flowed MacDonald Creek into Racing River, into Toad River, into Liard River. At about 170 miles was Muncho lake, a very beautiful sight. The road crossed the Liard at about mile 200 and went west until it came to Lower Post. Lower Post is still in British Columbia, about 25 miles below Yukon border. Watson Lake was about 25 miles inside Yukon. The lake here is used for seaplanes and the large sandy shore as an airport. The road follows a natural bed thru to Whitehorse and along a similar trail to Fairbanks.

The superhighway which, someday will be finished, is a marvel. Coming out in the fall, it was possible to ride over a lot of it. It is as straight as it can possibly be and varies very slightly in elevation. It is so hard and wide (up to 90 feet) and the shoulders slope away gradually 1′ in 15′ that cars travel 100 miles an hour down it. Its width is designed to allow aeroplanes to land on it. Through the mountains, this road has no greater grade than 5% whereas the tote road often has 12.5% grades. Further it goes quite straight, cutting off 3 or 4 miles in 7. In one case, it actually tunnels thru the peak of a mountain in order to maintain the grade.

On that road now, are running 10,000 trucks carrying supplies to Alaska. They are huge affairs that go 1 mile to a gallon. They carry a 4 ton payload and weigh 15 tons themselves. One interesting sight is to see 29-ton tankers which carry 15,000 gallons of gas. In the mountains they are drawn by army tanks being attached to the turret. All trucks have 10 drive wheels & front wheel drive.

Personally, they were a waste of money and steel. Along the road are many abandoned cats left because it was easier to get a new one than fix it. In the swamps are many buried because it was easier to leave them. In all the Americans were very wasteful and fool hardy.

It can be mentioned that the country is beautiful, large forests of spruce, jackpine, whitebirch and poplar. The Americans ruthlessly and carelessly burned the areas to speed the work. In the woods were untold numbers of black bears. These they constantly shot at for sport. As much as 100 in one week in one sector. The rivers were full of fish yet one man would boast of catching 90 of these in 3 hours. These fish were fish being 20 lb trouts, 10-15 lb grayling, lings. Everywhere were suckers of prodigious size.

But it is still our country, a country worth while holding on to. There is a wealth on pulpwood and hardwoods. Everywhere, there were traces of iron galena (lead) malachite (copper) and sulphur ores.

Any terms by which America would lay claim to those natural wealths would be detrimental to Canada. They would make us poor by their wasteful means of exploitation. They would do what they did this year, always manage to replace Canadians by Americans even at the expense of flying them from Washington, D.C. Yes money can do anything, but brains can to it better.

Remember, it is our country and being young we have our future with that country. Canada's future is in the north and fortune awaits our young men along Canada's great northern highway to Alaska.

Hope this will prove satisfactory. It is no hell, but I had to write fast and without preparation because of lack of time. Anyway it's already taken me 4½ hours.

Good-bye for now.

Mike

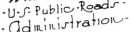

A Merry
Christmas
and
A Happy
New Year
from The Alaska-Canada Highway
Whitehorse-Yukon Territory-Christmas-1942
-U-S-Public-Roads-
-Administration-

THE ALCAN HIGHWAY
BUILT BY A WELCOME ARMY
OF U.S. SOLDIERS

Souvenir Folder of
Alaska Military
Highway

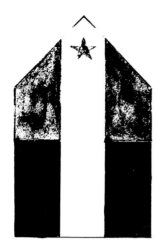

INAUGURATION
Northwest Service Command
Alaska - Canada - United States
Overland Mail Route
Via Alaska Highway
December 2, 1943
Fairbanks, Alaska to Whitehorse, Y.T.

Guiding the pipe dollies around steep and slippery curves and over narrow bridges was a severe test of the truck drivers' still. Sometimes the dollies jack-knifed, or pipe broke through the cabs, and there were a few casualties.

All color photos taken from Richard Finnie's book, CANOL (see Bibliography).

From CANOL Camp to Whitehorse 10 pumping stations were erected. At each were three Diesel engines, so designed that they could run on crude oil taken from the line, just as the gasoline engines along the supplementary lines between Whitehorse and Watson Lake and Fairbanks could tap the refined products as they flowed through.

Actual construction of the CANOL Road on the east side did not get underway until May 1943, when a lead crew set out from CANOL Camp and headed for the mountains a score of miles beyond. It was destined not to turn back until it met a similar crew from the west about seven months later.

Behind the road builders came the pipeliners, laying their pipe and welding it.

CANOL's operations extended not only into the Far North but westward nearly a thousand miles from Edmonton to rail's end at Prince Rupert and nearby Port Edward on the British Columbia coast. Here the Constructor built staging facilities for the shipping of supplies and equipment to southeastern Alaska and the Yukon. There was to be a large camp, wit' railroad spurs, warehouses, wharf, and tank farm. This was begun in October 1942.

Rainy, windswept Skagway was founded as the gateway to the fabulous Klondike during the Gold Rush of 1897-98, when it swarmed with adventurers. Afterwards it became a ghost town, surviving only as a small port and railroad terminal, attracting a few hundred tourists each summer. Suddenly, in the spring of 1942, it came to life again as a transfer point for troops and supplies for the Alaska Highway. Several months later it became a base of operations for the CANOL Project as well.

CANOL Camp was located away from the river on high ground, with barracks and warehouses and repair shops. As the work progressed and expanded, and the population grew finally to more than a thousand persons, another, larger, camp was built.

At intervals between Watson Lake and Carcross, and at other points along the Alaska Highway and access roads, camp after camp was built. In new and mostly uninhabited country there had to be camps for truck drivers and pipeliners as well as pumping-station builders and operators.

The Beginning and the End

Mile 0 at Dawson Creek, B.C.

Visitor Information Center and end of highway post at Delta Junction, Alaska. Delta Junction has been designated as the official end of the highway. DELTA CHAMBER OF COMMERCE

Mr. Max Bonnin,

5I5 East 24th. Street,

Minneapolis,

Minnesota.